MEG SALTER

Your Life

How Mindfulness Can Build Resilience
and Reveal Your Extraordinary

MegaSpace

The fruits of meditation, including this book, are dedicated

to my daughters, Jacqueline Grandy and Claire Grandy, and to

the memory of my brother John M.C. Salter

MegaSpace Press
Toronto, Canada
www.megsalter.com

Cataloguing data available from Library and Archives Canada
ISBN 978-0-9959368-0-5 (paperback)
ISBN 978-0-9959368-1-2 (ebook)

Produced by Page Two
www.pagetwostrategies.com
Cover and interior design by Peter Cocking
17 18 19 20 21   5 4 3 2 1

Advance praise for *Mind Your Life*

"The mainstreaming of mindfulness has become something of a fad. Unfortunately, many authors in that genre know much more about the mainstream than they do about the deep end of what mindfulness practice can deliver. Not so with Meg. She has practiced intensely for many decades. And she has personal experience of how a mindfulness practice can provide the 'big guns' that deliver the goods when all else fails.

"In this book, you will find evidence-based coaching strategies to help you turn good intentions into a sustainable practice. You will also find simple guidelines for customizing that practice using elements of Unified Mindfulness—a system widely respected for its comprehensiveness and conceptual clarity."

Shinzen Young

"My curiosity about meditation and mindfulness practices had been growing but *Mind Your Life* really provided the impetus and skills for incorporating it into my daily life and realizing the benefits. A great practical guide."

Scott Whitbread, partner, Stroud International

"A refreshingly practical and no-nonsense take on mindfulness, behaviour change and resilience, written by a life coach who understands the professional and family commitments of our busy modern age. Smart, scalable, with the potential to help a great many people."

Jeff Warren, meditation teacher and author of *The Head Trip: Adventures on the Wheel of Consciousness*

"Meg generously shares real-world wisdom in an inspiring and pragmatic way that coaches can use immediately with their overwhelmed clients."

Jill Malleck, Epiphany at Work, Integral Master Coach™ and OD Consultant

"*Mind Your Life* draws upon Meg's engaging personal journey to present a thoroughly modern approach for bringing the benefits of mindfulness practice to anyone. Accentuated with numerous intimate anecdotes, her approach distills the essential methodologies of contemporary researchers into a comprehensive system that is manageable, personal and ready to work for you."

Scott Nelson, CEO of noosworx

"No two people are alike. No two coaching programs are alike. Why should a path to greater mindfulness be any different? *Mind Your Life* offers a pragmatic approach to mindfulness that meets you right where you are! Useful. Relevant. Great variety of practices!"

Joanne Hunt, co-founder, Integral Coaching Canada®, Inc.

"Meg Salter has written a book that explores not just how to start a mindfulness practice but how to keep it going over the ebbs and flows of a lifetime. The stories of ordinary heroes help make it real and achievable. The steps and practices that Salter shares to help you bring mindfulness into your daily life are simple, for adults and children alike."

Kate Kerr, president of Wake Up Kate & mindfulness educator

Mind Your Life

———

Contents

Special Recognition

FOR MUCH of the subject matter of this book, I wish to deeply acknowledge Shinzen Young. He is a meditation master who freely offers his wisdom to many, encouraging others to spread it in their own voice. I have attended retreats with Shinzen since 2006, read most of his material and benefited from his personal guidance. The one who writes this book would not be here without him. His concepts and the methods of Unified Mindfulness are embedded throughout this book. Since it was not possible to reference these individually, I wish to do so now globally. You can find out more about Shinzen's work at www.shinzen.org or www.unifiedmindfulness.com.

I also want to thank Joanne Hunt and Laura Divine, Master Certified Coaches and founders of Integral Coaching Canada®, of which I am a graduate. The Integral Coaching Method® they have developed is based on an all-inclusive mode of human development that has become one of the foremost approaches to embodied change and coaching. This book draws on some elements of the Integral Coaching Method® to help the reader sustain the personal change that is everyday mindfulness. You can find out more at www.integralcoachingcanada.com.

Additional Thanks

I have been blessed with many teachers and wish to thank two who have made a lasting impression: Ken McLeod, a master of pointing out instructions, and Cynthia Bourgeault, whose earthy wisdom and deep erudition have breathed new life into my Christian roots. In writing this book, I have been surrounded by more support than I ever thought possible. There are so many to thank: Most importantly, my husband, John Grandy, whose love and support have been unquenchable for many years and who has trusted in me and this project when I did not. My mother, Ann Elizabeth Carson, whose journey to authorship has inspired so many. The ordinary heroes who permitted themselves to be interviewed and entrusted me with their stories. Janet Martin, Jennifer Smith, Jill Malleck, Marni Jackson, and Scott Whitbread, who offered their insights by reading early drafts. Patricia Pearson for her discerning editorial eye. Alexandra Shimo, Barbara Stubbs, Beverly Freedman, Bob Doering, Bonnie Foley-Wong, Debbie Dimoff, Eva Ticktin, Graham Byron, Janet Sims, Jeff Warren, Jo Roberts, Malti Mahajan, Michael Taft, Peter Pacini, Reggie Marra, Tim Hurson and Todd Mertz, who offered personal encouragement and practical support. My many clients and students, whose own "revealing of their extraordinary" is a constant source of inspiration. The team at Page Two Strategies, in particular Trena White, for taking on this project, and Amanda Lewis, for shepherding it through.

Introduction

I NEVER THOUGHT I would feel this comfortable in my own skin. What happened that transformed a stammering child into an adult who makes her living, as a coach and consultant, by talking? How did a timid person learn to enjoy challenge and change? Sure, I anticipated becoming hard working, studious and competent. But to experience moments of random joy, flashes of wicked humour, ease with uncertainty, the ability to meet total strangers without quivering? I never even imagined those possibilities.

Mindfulness is the difference that has *made* a difference. By now I have been practising meditation for over twenty years, and, unlike some teachers, I earned my stripes not by going away for periods of intensive study but in the midst of work and family life. So I know that you, too, can develop remarkable capacities while living your regular life.

This is a book that demonstrates how simple ways of altering how you pay attention can, with time and practice, change your life. But simple isn't always easy. Integrating a new habit in meaningful ways is a small but significant personal change in your life. I bring my background as an Integral Master Coach™ to help you make this change, turning your curiosity or intentions with regard to meditation into sustainable skills that will lead to personal flourishing. Why am I confident that you can do this? Because I have seen it in myself and others. Throughout this book, you will meet eighteen people who have been practising meditation for at least three years, some up to forty. By finding ways to persist in their practice, they all made themselves more resilient to challenges and more adaptable to change. Their stories attest to the deep capacities that mindful awareness unleashes, enabling ordinary people to live extraordinary lives.

A hot topic of research, mindfulness has been shown to reduce stress, improve overall well-being, re-wire the brain for focus and foster empathy and positive relationships. Mindfulness may prove to be for mental health what jogging was for physical health in the 1970s: an accessible way to improve well-being and vitality. Mindfulness is worth cultivating.

The mindfulness world has never been more ready for entry. It is right on a cusp, where second-generation approaches are building on the knowledge of the first generation of practitioners. The early adopters conducted a successful beta test. Centuries-old contemplative methods were recovered, re-worked for the modern, Western mind in a way that transcended religious beliefs or historic cultural practices. Contemporary science has validated that meditation produces measurable changes in the brain and body. The euphoria typical of early adopters (and opportunistic marketers) is now being translated into practical evidence. Healthy critical thinking is on tap. We know it isn't magic and that one size does not fit all. Instead, we know that mindfulness is evidence-based and customizable.

If you are finding that your ways of addressing persistent challenges don't seem to be working, you may be ready for a custom fit. How do you prevent constant stress from becoming *di*stress? How do you connect to your own inner voice in the midst of demands for 24/7 availability? How do you find restoration when Sundays (or Saturdays, or Fridays) are no longer days of rest? How do you pass on hope to your children in an era of low growth and tectonic global shifts? How do you meet your emotional, social or spiritual needs when your survival needs are sated?

This book is part of the second-generation approach to mindfulness. Many of the methods and concepts are based on the Unified Mindfulness System of Shinzen Young,[1] a fifty-year meditation teacher, author and science research consultant who has been a leading voice in the dialogues between East and West, spirituality and science.

Perhaps you thought that mindfulness means focusing on your breath while sitting on a cushion. Yes, that can be part of it; but it is by no means the only way.

Mindfulness can mean so many different things. Colloquially, it can refer to an attitude of being alert. Conceptually, mindfulness means paying attention to what's happening in the present moment in the mind, body and external environment, with an attitude of curiosity and kindness.[2] Practically, it can refer to different meditation methods and teaching protocols from respected teachers and traditions, ranging from the popular Mindfulness-Based Stress Reduction program to Mindfulness-Based Cognitive Therapy to Buddhist-inspired Vipassana meditation. All these methods develop capacities for focused attention on present-moment experience, with a suspension of judgement on what you are experiencing. All include one or more meditation practices, such as focus on the breath or on physical-body sensations. So why would I want to offer you yet another mindfulness system?

Because each of these valid approaches is also partial. They are based on one tradition, one teacher or one program that has selected specific techniques from a broad array of possibilities. They are effective for some people but not for all. So if you try one method and find it doesn't work, you may conclude that mindfulness is not for you. That's too bad, because you are missing out on a huge opportunity. It's like refusing to eat an array of vegetables because you have only been exposed to broccoli. What if a beautiful spinach salad hit the spot?

Shinzen Young's Unified Mindfulness is a meta-system that is both contemporary and classic. As a contemporary system it is secular, requires no particular belief background and is evidence-based, being tested in research labs such as Harvard Medical School and Carnegie Mellon. Yet the contemporary approach is grounded in classic wisdom traditions of both the East and the West. An umbrella framework like Unified Mindfulness has become possible only very recently, with the advent of global communications and sharing of cultural traditions from around the world.

This book is for all levels of experience. If you are inspired by wisdom literature, this will make it real in your life. If you want to try mindfulness—or have tried but been unable to keep it up—this will help you through the early learning curve. If you've been meditating for a while but have reached a plateau, it will give you new ways to revitalize your practice. Developing mindful awareness is a permanent change, but not a quick fix. With the right tools, support and some commitment on your part, you can do it. This book is here to help you. You can read it sequentially from beginning to end, dip in to the parts that interest you or refer to it later as a learning aid.

I will tell you my own story of resilience and change in Chapter 1, then in Chapter 2 introduce you to seven ordinary heroes: people who credit mindfulness practice for extraordinary outcomes in their lives, from coping with the emotional pain of post-traumatic stress disorder (PTSD) or the physical pain of ice-pick headaches to navigating business setbacks or moving beyond compassion fatigue. Chapter 3 gives a brief overview of the physical impacts of mindfulness on brain and body. Chapter 4 looks at the psychological impacts of mindfulness on resilience. (Mindfulness practice can act as a stress vaccine, activating the mental muscles that aid recovery, adaptation and change.) Then we move on to the nitty-gritty practicalities. In Chapter 5, we will look at mindfulness as a capacity to train attention.

You'll meet DAN—your default attentional network—and MoMo, the moment-by-moment sensory awareness that helps you unhook from DAN. I will give you a heads-up about the five main challenges in developing a sustainable mindfulness practice and a worksheet to help you anchor your motivation for practice. In Chapter 6, we'll review the Unified Mindfulness System, with its three fundamental attentional skills of concentration, sensory clarity and equanimity. Chapters 7, 8 and 9 give you a range of mindfulness practices, with clear instructions and examples of what the resulting experiences might look like "inside your head." While I will give you many options to choose from, don't get overwhelmed. You only need one method for an effective mindfulness practice. In Chapters 10 and 11, you'll meet more ordinary heroes, develop a customized roadmap for integrating mindfulness into your life and learn how to gauge progress in your own journey to personal flourishing.

I cannot promise you miracles; but I will say that if you mind your life—life has a way of minding you back.

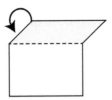

[1]

My Own Story

IN MANY ways, I won a lucky ticket in the lottery of life. Being born to two healthy parents at a time of peace and economic prosperity was a great start. As the eldest of four children in a close family, I never lacked for companionship or someone to boss around. I did well enough in school but not so much that I stood out. Summers were idyllic. For one whole month each summer, our family had a 2½ acre island to ourselves. We kids—two girls and two boys—ran around in glorious freedom: swimming, canoeing and, on rainy days, playing endless board games in the damp old cottage. There was a handmade target range down in the cedar grove where each of us did rifle practice. The boys loved to make an impressive sound, my sister preferred a bow and arrow. I was satisfied if I could make one mark on the target. I was a fortunate kid but shy, dreamy and physically awkward. I hung back in the playground, rarely joining the other girls in team sports or the dreaded skipping games. I was terrified of the math teacher, who required each child in turn to give out-loud answers to a row of sums on the blackboard. Long fantasy books provided an escape. By age nine, I was wearing pointy glasses. By age eleven, I stuttered so badly I could barely pronounce my friend's name, "Anita." It required all the courage I had to even call her on the phone. It was certainly a good enough childhood, stable but quirky.

Life got rougher in adolescence. Not just the usual pimples, but what was then called a "nervous breakdown" in my father. He disappeared for a few days, destination unknown, marital joint bank account empty, my mother in the lurch. He did return—from the British Virgin Islands—but then lost his job. His hidden alcoholism was exposed. My naïve trust in the adult world disintegrated. Subsequently, Dad regained his career, but our home was never the same. Eventually our parents divorced and my mother's chronic health problems worsened, even as she went back to school and then found work. A year after college, I married my dark-haired, Armenian boyfriend from high school. Four unhappy years later, we divorced.

Like most of us, I learned to cope with these everyday stresses and occasional traumas. By my thirties, I thought I had it figured out, the early turbulence safely behind me. I had a hot new husband (years later, he's still hot), a solid professional career in financial services, a five-year adventurous stint working in Europe and an MBA from a prestigious university. We were blessed with two healthy, wonderful daughters. When the girls were still young, I launched into consulting and coaching as a way to gain more flexibility in balancing the inevitable tensions of work and family life. Two big jobs, two healthy children, mortgage paid down. All good—right? Almost. Deep down, I felt I was putting up a good front. There were cracks and tensions in our family life. Despite family therapy, we did not have the perfect, loving home I'd wanted to create. One of our daughters was being bullied at school. Like every mother of young children, I felt maxed out and stretched thin. My coping strategy worked, a little. Head down, lean in, suck up your feelings to do what has to get done, small bouts of mild depression when overwhelmed.

Then, one sunny Saturday morning in April, the phone rang. On the surface, it was an ordinary weekend morning, hanging around the house with the girls after a busy work week, tidying up a bit. Except I had been waiting for three days to find out why my youngest brother, Johnnie, was missing. He'd driven his truck to work as usual but hadn't come home. The old .22 calibre rifle from Dad's estate, left to him four years earlier, was missing, too. "Oh God," we thought. "It has to be a coincidence." We knew Johnnie's life had been rough lately. Self-employed in the construction trades, he wasn't getting enough work; making his mortgage payments was difficult. We'd heard rumours of marital problems and of continued drug use after his roaring twenties. We hoped it was just a little weed, like we'd all done, but didn't really know. The previous Thanksgiving, when my brother Michael tried to engage him in conversation, Johnnie's wry sense of humour was missing. He sat on the couch, eyes downcast, answering in flat monosyllables.

Johnnie was a sweetheart of a guy: good-looking, intelligent, musical, a gifted gardener. He oozed languid physicality and had always had a girl around. He and his buddies were tight; they had one another's backs. The previous winter, when our mother had been ill, he'd shared care-giving duty with my sister, taking turns to drop in on Mom daily. He'd never hurt anyone in his life.

When the phone rang that Saturday morning, my brother Michael's voice was dull, wooden. Our sister, Hilary, had found

Johnnie's truck only a few blocks from his home. Opening up the door, she found him dead. He'd been lying in the back of the truck for a whole day; he shot himself through the head with the rifle. Later we found a tape in his house, an auditory suicide note: "I've made a mess of things," he said. "You'll be better off without me." He could find no way out, no hope. A week later, we found he'd timed his suicide so his wife could make a claim while the insurance policy was still valid. Johnnie had made his arrangements with customary workmanlike precision. For the rest of us, for me and all those who loved him, that was the day that each of us shattered.

What do we do when hit by traumatic events? We use whatever strategies we've developed so far. For the next few months, I coped the way I'd always done. I tried to be honest by speaking about the unspeakable with my children and friends. As a newly self-employed consultant, I didn't want to take much time off work. So I swallowed my feelings in order to get done what had to get done, kept busy to bear the unbearable. Only music could unlock my heart. When my brother's musician friends played the old rock tune "Johnny B. Goode" at his wake, I could finally cry.

One day, I heard a voice. Five months after Johnnie's death, alone in our bedroom, I heard a distinct little voice in my head. "You should meditate," it said, "or you could end up like John." The voice had a unique quality. Few words, low tone, big impact. Enough that I can recall the scene vividly, twenty years later. The voice came again a week later: "You should meditate." I now know that this kind of insight comes from penetrating clarity, when we are shaken open to our depths, able to hear the still, small voice within. At the time, all I knew was that I had better listen.

Why that "or else" threat? Superficially, there were big differences between us. He was the youngest; I was the oldest. He was struggling more than we were. But he was my baby brother; despite the age gap, we had shared occasional but deep moments of connection. He got married in our backyard. He was the beloved godfather to our younger daughter, who adored sleepovers at Uncle Johnnie's house.

Whether caused by clinical depression or situational despair, traumas like suicide can happen in any family. In some families more than others, there is a heritable component in suicides. In the family of author Ernest Hemingway, there were five suicides over four generations. On both sides of my family run long lines of alcoholism, a slow, tortuous form of self-destruction. Something inside me knew I had better get real. That little voice was telling me that I had better build resilience or some nameless horror could just as easily grab me or mine.

I had a passing familiarity with meditation. I'd tried it out once in undergraduate days, visiting the Zen Center in Rochester, New York, for a day. But I was turned off by what seemed like a ritualized, otherworldly lifestyle. Now, prompted by the voice, I asked around for a recommendation and through a friend found a teacher of Mindfulness-Based Stress Reduction (MBSR). The MBSR program was developed in the 1980s by Dr. Jon Kabat-Zinn at the University of Massachusetts Medical School and is now widely associated with the practice of mindfulness. You may have heard of Kabat-Zinn's many books, including *Full Catastrophe Living*. After an eight-week course, I set up a daily twenty-minute period to meditate, right after the girls went off to school in the morning and before I started work. If nothing else, I figured it was some time for myself.

And I hated it, almost every minute of it. The practice I had been given was breath counting. Pay attention to the breath, counting each breath from one to ten, starting over at one if you lose track. After a while, I found I could maintain enough focus not to lose track. But the side effects were brutal. Halfway into my twenty minutes, I began feeling an itchy-crawly "jumping outta my skin" sensation. If as a child you ever had an "ants in the pants" feeling, or if your fingers or toes tingled when you came indoors out of the cold, that's the sensation. What I didn't know was that when you create space for your inner experiences to surface, all kind of tensions you didn't even know you had can come along for the ride.

So my early learning curve was bumpy. Things got worse before they got better. Whether through bull-headed determination, the shock of John's death or the reverberation of the voice, I did manage to persevere through the first few months of itchy-crawlies. Within six months, it dawned on me that something was different. I was changing, although I hadn't expected to. (At that time, mindfulness teaching focused on stress reduction and calming.) Meanwhile, I was coping with a major life transition with less blaming and more courage than I ever had before.

Around this time, my husband and I had decided, for professional but mostly family reasons, that we needed to relocate to a different city. My husband worked for an international bank. We were used to company-sponsored moves, as we'd already done three of them. So we hoped we could arrange for another corporate transfer to the city of our choice, especially if he asked really nicely! After months of lobbying, it became obvious a transfer was not going to be offered. If we wanted this new life, we would have to do it ourselves. Both of us would have to find new jobs and pay for the relocation. To top it off, we were trying to sell our house in a sinking housing market. It took us six months to find a buyer. We lowered the asking price three times, losing over thirty percent of the value of our only asset. Aiming for a

September start date for new schools for our daughters, we put
in an offer on a home in our new city before we had sold our current house or had any cash—or had even landed any jobs.

I had never before had the nerve to take on this much risk
or to go through such prolonged uncertainty. Meditation, however, was teaching me a core muscle of resilience: the ability to
tolerate difficult feelings, whether emotional anxiety or physical
itchy-crawlies. Not being overwhelmed by my feelings meant
I could persist through ambiguity and loss, not giving up hope
for our goal. Facing myself meant I didn't project my fears on to
others as much. Practically, this meant I stopped pestering my
husband ("When are you going to get that transfer?") or blaming him for a situation clearly beyond his control. Less nagging
meant we were able to stay connected through a stressful time.
(Since then, my husband is all in favour of meditation, although
he personally doesn't indulge.)

Since those early attempts, I have practised meditation in
a variety of traditions. Like physical fitness, meditation comes
from many backgrounds, teaches different kinds of exercises,
by teachers who each bring their own style. Over a twenty-year
period I have experienced the benefits, the pitfalls and the pla-
teaus of any long-term endeavour.

About a year after our successful relocation (new home, two
new schools, two new jobs), a friend suggested I join her at a
local church. It was a busy Protestant congregation with many
activities. One in particular intrigued me; I had never heard of
Christian Meditation. Founded in 1975 by the Benedictine monk
John Main, the core practice of Christian Meditation is not the
breath, but a mantra, a word or phrase that you silently repeat.
John Main learned about mantra from an Indian monk when
he was stationed in Malaya with the British diplomatic service,

before he took up religious orders. Part of the global burgeoning of contemplative practice, The World Community for Christian Meditation is now led by Father Laurence Freeman. It encompasses groups that meet in churches, homes and even prisons, in more than one hundred countries.

Here I learned not only a different method but a different purpose. While stress reduction is important, meditation can link to deeper values. For the first time, I experienced practising in a group. On Sunday mornings, a few of us would settle into chintz-covered chairs for forty-five minutes of silent practice and a period of conversation. My restless mind and body settled more quickly. Perhaps due to early shyness, I have never been much of a group person. So the value and support of a group was a revelation to me. Who knew that companionship and communication don't necessarily depend on words?

I continued in this way for the next three years. By now meditation had become a maintenance habit. The itchy-crawlies had long ceased. Most days, during my sits I experienced some calm, which spilled over into daily life as we settled into our new home. When I, along with others, got laid off in a corporate downsizing, I had a go-to coping strategy. My sits were not calm because I brought the sensations of doubt, worry and questions to them. But at least I had a place to contain the stress, to fully face both my fears and my hopes. It meant I didn't vent on other people or take action prematurely.

It was during this transition period from a full-time job to a coaching and consulting practice that I discovered Buddhist meditation practices. One Sunday morning, someone handed me a brochure for a local yoga and meditation centre. In a nondescript midtown office building, I found a small suite of rooms decorated with a Tibetan altar, colourful prayer flags and embroidered cloth paintings. A strange and exotic setting, but with friendly and sincere people. I also found, for the first time, a teacher. Buddhism understands meditation training as a path with discernible markers along the way. I found a teacher who had gone down this path considerably farther than me, who could provide practical instruction, inspirational teaching and one-on-one guidance, pointing out where I was stuck and how I might move forward. She had three grown children of her own, so I could relate to her. Her energy, kindness and bright red toenails were attractive to me.

Here I learned more practices: compassion, gratitude and visualizations. I learned to become mindfully aware not only of the thinking mind but also the feeling body, with its subtle patterns of tension and pulses of energy. I learned to broaden meditation from something I did at a set time and place to a practice that I could interject throughout the day—walking the dog, waiting in line, during a conversation. Importantly, through regular meditation retreats, I learned to go deep.

Meditation retreats may sound like a withdrawal from life, but actually they help you to engage with life more fully. You put aside many of your usual activities in order to practise intensively. You unplug from your devices and distractions to connect more deeply with yourself and others. With nothing to distract you, you get to experience yourself and the people and circumstances around you just as they are. While each teacher has her or his own style, all retreats involve a combination of teaching, extended practice, periods of silence, help with household tasks, group dialogue, music or ritual.

Initially I found retreats quite challenging. I experienced my personal patterns of agitation (a subtler version of the itchy-crawlies), "driven-ness" and a preference for speed and efficiency. Once, I even got a speeding ticket driving up to retreat! "That'll be $140 and four demerit points, Ma'am." The thoughts and memories that came up during meditation were sometimes painfully poignant: Johnnie, childhood scenes, memories of births and deaths, failures and triumphs. But usually they were ho-hum, like watching an old movie rerun for the umpteenth time. Regardless, after a week of retreat, I always felt better. I seemed to cope more effortlessly with life in the months that followed. I did not turn into a different person (my husband's concern) but found it easier to be myself. Retreat practice has now become the bedrock of my personal stability, important enough that I schedule regular periods into my calendar, ranging from half-day to week-long events.

After some years with that group, I found myself bumping into the limits of a traditional belief system overlaid, patchwork fashion, on to modern life. I needed to see greater relevance to the contemporary challenges and pace of life. I wanted a more integrated approach, big enough to include a variety of practice modalities, deep enough to touch the taproot of wisdom traditions. In 2006, I started studying with Shinzen Young, who brought both the breadth and depth I was seeking. His methods and concepts have been a core component of my practice and teaching ever since.

I knew both from reading and from meeting remarkable people that extraordinary outcomes were possible. But I wanted to experience this kind of flourishing within the life I had, both for myself and the people I loved. The Unified Mindfulness System makes this kind of deep practice available for ordinary people. You don't need a natural talent for meditation, but you do have to be clever in how you go about cultivating it—which Young's Unified Mindfulness allows.

I started by thinking meditation was like a special trick or tool I could use. Now I understand it to be our ordinary capacities, carefully honed. I started by seeking desperately needed calm and relief from stress. Now this has generalized to base levels of mindfulness skills that are permanently elevated, so that focused attention and open presence are available all day long. I started by treating mindfulness as a separate practice that I carefully nurtured and protected. Now I appreciate that mindfulness is a foundational capacity for many other skills and capabilities, including the ability to be fully present with a client, without judgment or a racing mind. I started with one method that I practised for a set time each day. Now I have multiple methods that I can call on throughout the day.

Trust me, you can practise anywhere, anytime.

I have practised with Radiohead or Sex Pistols blaring in the background as the girls got ready for school. I have practised by fully savouring the pleasures of life, such as music, chocolate or sunsets. I have practised by focusing on sights and sounds while driving the car, which is a nice way to get in practice time on ordinary days but the only way to drive in heavy snow or rain. I have practised by focusing attention on my tense jaw, thereby realizing that the grinding was happening during the day, not the night, and so didn't require a night-guard for TMJ (temporomandibular jaw disorder). I have practised in a toilet stall for a few minutes before a big meeting, taking a few deep breaths to calm a racing heart and mind. I have practised in the middle of a workshop I was facilitating for fifty research oncologists that was about to go sideways. I paused for a few seconds, with literally no idea what to do next but very little emotional panic. Then someone opportunely volunteered the perfect suggestion. I have practised during showdowns with my teenage kids, facing and completely feeling my anger, then expressing myself with a clean force that didn't carry bitterness or vengeance.

Mindfulness helped me through the normal bumps of life, including three layoffs (one for me and two for my husband), teenage dramas, boardroom tensions, the uncertainty of entrepreneurship, the dementia and dying of our elders and mental health issues on both sides of our family.

It also helped with the trauma of Johnnie's death. A wound like this creates a hole. You are never the same again. (Would you want to be?) Eventually, the wound scars over. But for some people, the wound can go septic, festering for their whole life. With my original coping strategy of disengaging and keeping busy, this was a real risk. But it didn't happen. The opening created by that hole has slowly morphed into a compassion for suffering that was not there before.

With less energy absorbed by repetitive stress and occasional shocks, there is more energy for unsuspected inner potential to emerge. To my relief, I find that with the passage of time, I'm not bitter but better. I've been able to let go—forgive—the hurts done to me—even harder, the hurts I have done to others. I am more comfortable with ambiguity, able to rest in that creative space of possibility between the old and the new. With the emergence of inner quiet—like the diminishing of mental radio static—I am more able to detect the subtle signals of the small voice within or make contact with the vital energies of the body or connect deeply with others. Some of this may be random luck; but much of it I can only attribute to a sustained mindfulness practice. Transformation has been real.

[2]

Stories of Ordinary Heroes

MINDFULNESS MEANS learning to pay attention to what's happening in the present moment in the mind, body and external environment, with an attitude of curiosity and kindness.[3] It sounds simple, doesn't it? At later stages, it is. But at first, it may not be easy. In my experience, and that of many mindfulness teachers, about one in ten people who takes a mindfulness course continues practising on a regular basis. A recent study confirmed this.[4] One year after taking a Mindfulness-Based Stress Reduction course, ten percent of participants were regularly doing formal practices like breath meditation or body scans, although a larger proportion were practising informally during the day. Why is there so little take-up?

Developing mindful awareness means going against our built-in mental attentional patterns and what's known as our brain's "default attentional network." Mindful awareness can feel counterintuitive, like trying to float a boat upstream. My coaching training and experience tells me that, like any new habit, developing a sustainable mindfulness practice involves a small but significant behaviour change. Engineering this change involves several factors. These include the degree of stress or challenge we are coping with, the vision we have of what is possible (is our vision inspiring yet realistic?), the range of practical techniques we understand and can implement and the experience of positive rewards for our efforts.

Despite the challenges, many people *do* manage to make it work. Let's investigate these positive role models, people who have practised mindfulness and integrated it into their lives in a sustainable way. Each has been practising meditation for at least three years, some for up to forty years. They come from all walks and stages of life, from the recently graduated to the recently retired, from government employees to entrepreneurs. They include a teacher, a legal secretary, a psychologist, a doctor, academics, writers, corporate executives and a massage therapist. None of them is rich or famous.

They all had to find their own way in to navigating the learning curve. They started, stopped then restarted practice. They varied their mindfulness techniques. They found helpful supports for their practice. They found ways to integrate practice into their day. They developed a more nuanced expectation of what is involved and how long it may take to change your brain. They made a point of noticing small but permanent changes in their lives. They came to enjoy daily practice.

Through finding ways to consistently practise and apply mindfulness skills, these ordinary individuals have achieved extraordinary lives. Theirs are stories of struggle and adaptation, of resilience in the face of challenge leading to unexpected flourishing. I asked them how they got started and continued, what the impact on their lives has been and what advice they would give to you. First, I'd like you to meet Nicola, Alex, Barbara, Brian, James and Lara.

Nicola: Beyond Stress Reduction

Nicola is a dark-haired woman whose lilting accent with vivacious tones hearkens back to her native Romania. Trained as a physician, she left a repressive Communist regime with her husband for a new life in North America in the 1990s. When she found she couldn't practise as a physician here, she retrained as a physiotherapist. Nicola now works with stroke rehabilitation patients. She has been practising mindfulness for ten years.

How did you start and then continue mindfulness?
"As a doctor, I had heard of the positive effects of mindfulness, but I had no time to practise. Of course, it would have been unthinkable in a Communist regime.

"When I divorced, it came to me that meditation was something that I could do to help myself. So I found a tea shop in town; every week they had a different meditation teacher. I found out there's a lot more to it than I thought. I started with basic breath practice. I was so motivated at first. I'm just going to glue my bum to the chair! But I found it so frustrating. Why can't I do it? I'm breathing, so why don't I relax? I'm used to working hard so this lack of results was puzzling. When did being uncomfortable ever stop me before?

"Then I looked further into the scientific evidence. I knew my brain was changing, so this encouraged me to continue. I realized what I was experiencing was psychological discomfort, not body discomfort. I did continue, but I was very erratic at first, from five to fifteen minutes.

"Several months after my divorce, I did a one-day meditation retreat and had a real 'aha' moment. At the beginning of the day, I was so restless I just wanted to throw the sitting cushion out the window. Then I found myself sobbing, howling. Why? It came to me that I was feeling guilty for leaving my husband. I didn't want to face it. I was so devastated and so happy. That moment stayed with me for the longest time. It gave me validation.

"After a while, I began to feel some relaxation after some of the sits. It took me two to three years to settle into a steady thirty-minute practice. I've always believed there is way more to our bodies and minds than we can fix with a pill, so I'm glad I took it easy like this.

"My mindfulness practice still isn't consistent. With my chaotic schedule, I can't make a regular routine. I find it fantastically helpful to have a variety of techniques, like walking meditation or loving-kindness practice. I can tailor my practice to my day and whatever I'm going through. If I'm talking with a friend, I'll focus totally on listening and being present. It's so interesting because it makes me aware of so many things I never noticed, like how intense my emotional reactions are. I often do driving practice in the car. If I'm frustrated being stuck in traffic, then it's one more chance to practise. Recently, my motivation has changed. Now if I haven't meditated for a few days, I feel so horrible. I know that if I don't keep up some continuity, I won't get the good moments."

What has been the impact on your life?

"My arguments with people I care about are different now. I notice the intensity of my own emotional reaction to others; I can hear the voice in my head yelling at me.

"'Just tone it down!' I tell myself. So I don't react to others the way I used to. They notice it and their behaviour changes, too. I still find fault with myself but not as much as before.

"It's also had a big effect on my clinical work in stroke rehabilitation. Being told you've had a stroke, you'll never walk again—that's really hard. People can collapse, cry; they may be angry or in denial. It makes a big difference if you can say to them, 'Okay, let's just sit here and talk about it.'"

What advice would you give to others?
"Try it. Find a way that suits you. It may be boring at first but it does get better, so stick to it. Don't give up because of one method or one teacher. You have to find your own path."

Alex: Recovery from PTSD

Alex is a writer with an interest in Indigenous issues, recently settled into marriage and motherhood.[5] Five years ago, when she was struggling with post-traumatic stress disorder, life was more chaotic.

How did you start and then continue mindfulness?
"As part of my book research, I spent some time at Kashechewan, an Indigenous reserve on the shores of James Bay in northern Canada. It was such a hard place to live. I witnessed child abuse, youth suicide. I was the target of homophobia. I was trying to help others but I found myself feeling helpless. I witnessed such extreme despair that I got burned. On my return, I was suffering from flashbacks, so I signed up to see a PTSD specialist and was on his waitlist. I was lucky that a friend of mine, Jeff Warren, was teaching meditation. I took an eight-week mindfulness course where we learned a variety of techniques. Then I started

to practise daily for fifteen minutes. Later that year, I went on a one-week retreat and had one intense experience. I became aware that I was carrying a lot in my chest, so I just stayed focused on the chest area for two hours. I could feel my chest cavity actually opening.

"I was lucky that I felt the impact of mindfulness right away, both emotionally and physically. When the flashbacks were triggered, I could just stay present with them. I found the intensity of what I was experiencing went down. I was able to disentangle the flashback experience into its mental, visual and body components, so it became much less overwhelming. I kept practising mindfulness techniques because they helped with my flashbacks. Also, I came off antidepressants and the steroids I'd been on for five years for my asthma.

"Now I sit with this local group once a week. I find the support from others is really important. On my own, I'll practise for twenty to thirty minutes most days. If I'm going through a rough period, I'll try to sit for ninety minutes on the weekend. Now I'm at the point where I can't go without it. If I miss two days, I start to feel overwhelmed. When I'm practising mindfulness, it's like my thoughts are a stream; I'm trying to sit on the bank of the river, not getting caught up in the story."

What has been the impact on your life?
"Creatively, I found that my writing exploded after learning mindfulness. As a writer, you have to get to a point where you can read your material like an objective person. Mental chatter is a distraction and now I know how not to get caught up in that.

"Personally, I'm not afraid to do anything anymore. Whatever happens, I know I have methods I can go to. So when someone says something bad to me, I see how the reaction occurs in my body and I can let it go. I'm also less attached to outcomes.

There's so much in an outcome that is out of your hands. When I get too 'grippy' about it, I know I'm less present and so make poorer choices. You just have to put your best effort out there and not hold on too tightly.

"Overall, I find I'm calmer and more focused. I'm more aware of my unconscious drivers. I can catch a thought and question, 'Is this what I want my motivation to be?' My friends say I'm less impulsive. I have deep emotions. Before, I would need to act on them to release them. Now I can be aware of what's arising without having to act on it. You realize a lot of these drivers are not really part of you; they're funny. A sense of lightness starts to open up."

What advice would you give to others?

"Learning mindfulness is like learning to play a violin. When you start, you sound awful. You think you'll never make real music. But you've heard good music before, so you know where you need to go. With the violin, would you expect to go from the sound of scratchy cat wailing to symphony-calibre music in one week? Of course not. The same thing applies to mindfulness. At first it feels like a total waste of time; but it will get better. So don't be too hard on yourself. Take it in the spirit of play! You don't have to believe in anything; just become more aware of what's in your brain."

Barbara: Navigating a Business Setback

Barbara speaks to me with intensity and forthrightness. Leveraging her background in nursing and finance, she started her own company in the health care sector. She is proud of its contributions and accomplishments, including winning awards for best workplace and being a top fifty company in her state. Five years ago, she felt compelled to protect her business—and the sixty employees who worked there. An employee had left the firm, taking many of its trade secrets and the largest client. Barbara launched a lawsuit. This challenge led her to seek out mindfulness.

How did you start and then continue mindfulness?
"I had to protect the company from going under, both for myself and for my employees. I knew I would need something to help with my emotional well-being during that period. I was determined not to follow my usual patterns of anger, so I sought a therapist who also taught mindfulness. This counsellor gave me faith. If I was serious, I had to meditate for twenty minutes, twice a day.

"I'm sure I'm at the high end of ADD. My brain was so unmanageable it took me hours to calm down. At first, I had to go to a quiet room in my house and listen to tapes with no other distractions around me. Sometimes I had to sit for five to six hours to get even two minutes of feeling calm. I had to learn how to quiet my brain. Over that seven months of the lawsuit, it got better and better.

"After we won the lawsuit, I realized it would take us a long time to recoup our costs and recover commercially. Our key employees all have equity in the firm, so success is important not just to me. I was able to be very calm through this recovery period, understanding it would be okay whether or not we recovered commercially. This helped me to lead our team back to success.

"Now when I practise mindfulness, I can get into that calm, fluid state quite quickly. I practise a variety of techniques, like calming practices, gratitude meditations or breathing exercises to disrupt the anxious brain. Calming is a go-to practice. It helps you realize how much bigger the world is, how connected we all are. There are activities I do every day to ground myself. Sometimes it's just telling myself, 'Today every time I wash my hands, I'm going to be in the moment.'

"For ADD people like myself, mindfulness has to be tied to a specific activity. [A direction like] 'Just follow your breath' may not be the best tool for them. You have to start with the concentration skill. ADD people are never going to get to clarity and equanimity until they can concentrate."

What has been the impact on your life?
"During the lawsuit, I was able to stay emotionally balanced, which helped me glide through the whole process more peacefully. It took all of my energy to do this, but I did. I never hated. My attorney said people in similar situations suffer huge emotional breakdowns; mindfulness helped me avoid that.

"After the lawsuit was over, I realized I wanted to learn more about this, so three years ago, I took a Mindfulness-Based Stress Reduction teacher training course. Now I teach meditation monthly in my home to local women; we meditate for around forty minutes, then have dinner. It's a supportive and beautiful part of my life. They all say it has changed their lives. One of my friends was dying; she actually became a beacon of light during that time. Another friend's husband left her, and thanks to meditation she became a changed woman—for the better.

"Mindfulness has changed me. All that time I put into meditation has rewired my brain in a permanent way. I went from never finishing a task to finishing tasks purposely. I couldn't even blow-dry my hair and keep the blow-dryer on one place. Now I can. I used to have severe fibromyalgia. Now I'm almost in complete remission. It was so bad I couldn't even beat eggs with a whisk. Now I can barely remember what that's like. My friends see a difference, too. They say I'm more compassionate, calmer, more detail-oriented. Meditation has been what makes life beautiful, robust and meaningful. It has allowed me to play in the business world with a lighter touch. It helps me realize how much bigger the world is, how connected we all are."

What advice would you give to others?
"For ADD people like me, I wouldn't recommend going cold turkey, the way I did! A busy mind needs to be kept busy, so I would teach simple daily activities where you can build the skill of concentration. Things like washing your hands while being in the moment. Mindfulness is not easy but it is rewarding. When people say they're not good at it, I say they're human. No one is good until they practise. It's like getting out of bed and saying you're going to run a marathon. It doesn't happen that way. Take little steps every day and stitch them together over time."

Brian: Equanimity or Death

Brian has a calm demeanour, wry smile and twinkly eyes. At age sixty-one, he effortlessly puts in sixty-hour weeks in the film business. Meeting him, you would see no signs of the recent torment in his life. Brian started meditating as a young man, first exploring altered states of consciousness, then slowly gravitating to Zen-style meditation practice. He found it helped get him through the rough spots in life. It left him with a greater sense of purpose, connection, a deeper love for life. So when the headaches started in April 2012, he had something to fall back on.

**How did this most recent phase of
your meditation practice start?**

"I was working on a video project in production when I started
getting ice-pick headache attacks. From there, it quickly went to
full-blown atypical trigeminal neuralgia."

Trigeminal neuralgia is a chronic pain condition affecting the
nerve that carries sensation from the face to the brain. Even mild
stimulation of the face, such as brushing your teeth, may trigger a jolt of excruciating pain. While the attacks may initially be
short, they can progress, causing longer, more frequent bouts of
searing pain. Treatment options typically include medications,
injections or surgery. About his headaches, Brian explains:

"The atypical version that I had is so rare there isn't much
research on it. Anyone with it will do just about anything to end
that pain, including taking their own life. That's why it is called
the suicide disease. I did try some of the medications, but they
made me feel ill and disconnected. I was no longer able to work.
My executive function had disappeared. I couldn't speak. I literally could no longer think. I was forced to retire and live off
my savings. The illness was so acute I couldn't make contact
with my head on any surface—even a pillow—without triggering intense stabbing attacks. So in May, one month after the
headaches started, I tried meditation, using a breath-counting
method, to see if this would help. When I focused all my attention on the breath, I found the pain was manageable. But
the minute I stopped, the pain came back full on. I did this for
up to twenty hours a day, just to survive. I had pain all the time.
Plus anxiety, which was as difficult as the pain. Was this going to
be my lot in life forever? I knew I had a choice: become a zom-
bie with drugs and surgery, commit suicide or stay present with
the pain.

"As a trained therapist, I knew I was going to need some help, so I sought a psychologist who specialized in post-traumatic stress. He introduced me to the Unified Mindfulness methods of Shinzen Young. One of the key messages is that *'suffering = pain x resistance.'* If I could reduce my resistance to the pain, then perhaps my actual suffering would diminish. To do this, I had to employ a different meditation strategy. I had to turn toward the pain and face it, not turn away as I had been doing.

"So that night as I lay down in bed, I thought, 'I am going to experience nonresistance.' When I felt the stabbing attacks, instead of turning away from the pain sensations by focusing on the breath, I turned toward the experience, relaxing into it as best I could. After a while, I felt a tingling at the tip of my toes, which moved up and down the whole body, back and forth, rocking me in this flow of ecstatic love. I was pretty skeptical at first. 'Did that just happen?' I wondered. As if to answer, the experience started again. I was in a bliss state for quite a while; the extreme opposite end of what I'd been living with. Later, the pain returned but not nearly with the same intensity as before. I realized that I'd had a peak experience; I would need to make an investment for this to become a lasting experience.

"I started working with these methods regularly, including weeks of intense retreat practice. When I was sitting in meditation, I was pain free. Later, I learned how to carry these methods into daily life. I was starting to rewire my brain and my relationship to pain. I learned to have complete equanimity, because whenever I was not in equanimity, I was hit by pain immediately!"

What has been the impact on your life?
"Now I'm working again, up to twelve to fourteen hours a day in the film business. People will say to me, 'You're a machine. You

don't get distracted by anything unless you choose to.' That's right. The concentration ability I've developed just spills over effortlessly into work. While I'm working, the pain is there, but I use the Focus Out meditation technique [see Chapter 8], so the pain is in the background, not bothering me. When I stop working, the pain comes back, so I have to do the practice. The pain keeps me exactly in the present moment.

"I've changed in other ways, too. My wife would say my depth of understanding and courage has increased. Courage because suicide was always an option. I used to use lots of rackets in order to get along with people. Now I'm much more honest, more direct. I don't swallow things as much. I used to be really angry, even disillusioned, with us humans as a species. Now I have a greater patience and love for humankind. In mindfulness, you begin to see more of what really is: your true self."

What advice would you give to others?
"All of us are getting older and will have to face the challenges and transitions that aging brings, whether our own health or the loss of loved ones. We may be prepared for that—or not. We may not all go out with happy smiles on our faces! People can grieve for the rest of their lives because they don't have the skills to cope with those difficult emotions. Meditation is *not* about not being human; it's about experiencing emotions fully, without grasping or pushing them away. Shit happens and mindfulness helps you deal with that. The skills you develop in mindfulness—concentration, sensory clarity, equanimity—can also help you function better in daily life, from work to sport to parenting."

James: Coping with Compassion Fatigue

James is an emergency physician who has also explored the world. As a young man travelling around Asia, he was attracted to Buddhist philosophy, so he started practising meditation on his own, using the breath-counting method. He had some deep experiences, felt very close to God and knew that in some profound way his life had shifted. But then it was back to the hectic life of a medical resident, living at the hospital, working all hours. He and a colleague used to encourage each other to find the time to meditate, but in this environment it was hard to do. After a move to another city, his meditation practice pretty much disappeared.

Then, in 2007, James set out for a six-month stint with Doctors Without Borders, a global medical and humanitarian relief organization, in the contested border town of Abyei, Sudan. He spent his days treating malnourished children, coping with a measles epidemic and watching for war. Worn thin by the struggle to meet overwhelming needs with few resources, he returned home more affected by the experience than he had anticipated. He wrote of his experiences in *Six Months in Sudan*.[6]

How did you get started again in meditation?
"This time, I had a specific reason for practice. A friend asked me, 'How are you going to stay close to your original intention in writing this book, without getting distracted by all the attention you will get?' Having a meditation practice helped me to tell the story as nakedly as possible, to stay in touch with my commitment to humanitarian work.

"In 2011, when I worked again for Doctors Without Borders, this time in Somalia, I wanted to see if I could go through the experience and not be so sickened by it. So I meditated every day, twice a day. There are very few moments of quiet in a refugee camp. I took one hour before breakfast for meditation and yoga, then tried to fit in more time later in the morning, before it got really hot and busy. By this time, I was using some of the Unified Mindfulness methods. Mindfulness enabled me to be more effective in a way that didn't diminish my competence or my compassion. It allowed me not to get used up all the time. There's such a wellspring of strength and vulnerability once you're able to work from that place. I was able to mourn deeply, then leave the mission with none of the prior regrets I'd carried out with me from Sudan.

"As an emergency room doctor, I meditate every day in the morning. First, I have to caffeinate myself, then I'll spend from twenty to forty minutes using a variety of meditation methods. My wife and I meditate together, so I really enjoy that. But the big difference has been mindful moments throughout the day. This could be while walking down the hallway to a patient's room or preparing myself for the difficult conversations that are an inevitable part of emergency medicine."

What has been the impact on your life?
"I can't imagine a greater opportunity that one could miss than an opportunity to be really clear in every moment of your life. People talk about doctors getting hardened, cold or detached. But I find I'm able to be more loving and forgiving of myself and others. I'm less bummed out by the suffering, even though I see lots of it. There's a humility that comes from touching beyond the knowing mind; we realize how much we'll never know, how ephemeral our experiences are."

What advice would you give to others?

"Like anything where you want to make progress, mindfulness requires a commitment of time and effort. The outcomes may not be an instant difference for everyone. You have to learn to be okay with that. Equanimity is part of everyone's practice, at one point or another. Try to sit for at least a little bit every day. Find a teacher who speaks to you, or a community of support. Actively try to detect little changes in your life, not just in you but in how people respond to you. Are there things that you used to find challenging where you now experience a little more ease? Perhaps you're not as freaked out as usual? Then hold that direction. If you experience some quiet during meditation, then fall into it. You have to keep creating opportunities to cultivate new neural pathways. But ultimately the goal is not some special state but to become a person who consistently demonstrates admirable behaviour."

Lara: Navigating Underemployment

In her mid-thirties, Lara works in a busy communications agency; the same one she left earlier, in her late twenties, to pursue her passion for education and social justice. She went to teachers' college, but one year after graduating had not yet found a job. She was caught up in that one-third of graduates unable to find steady work in the education system. What she did find was a contract position leading a program in a low-income suburban school. On her first day, she broke up two different fist fights. Her pittance of a salary didn't cover rent, let alone groceries. With this kind of stress, she found herself reverting to bad old habits of weekend drinking and disordered eating. Going back to her communications agency job solved the money issues but left her with a resigned disappointment that she might never be able to do what she so longed for. Lara was first exposed to meditation as a child.

"When I was a kid, my father tried to teach me meditation methods for my pre-exam anxiety. I thought it was the stupidest thing in the world."

She read about Buddhism in high school and in university had tried out a few silent retreat days. It was intriguing enough that Lara dabbled in different meditation groups and tried to practise on her own. But with a busy schedule, her practice was sporadic. The tipping point came when she met a group that appealed to her.

How did you start and then continue with mindfulness?

"I teach fitness on the side and one day a woman came up to me and asked, 'Do you meditate?'

"'I try to, but I'm not very diligent.'

"'Well, you should check out The Consciousness Explorers Club. They're a different kind of group.'"

Situated in Toronto's hip Little Italy neighbourhood, The Consciousness Explorers Club bills itself as a non-profit meditative think tank and community hub that supports personal growth through meditation and social practices. Lara is one of those people whose motivation comes from being with the right community. In this group, she had found her people.

"I started off going to weekly classes. It probably took a year before I could develop a steady practice on my own at home. One day, I went to class with a friend and found I'd got the day wrong. The place was closed. So my friend and I went to the park and I guided us through an hour-long meditation. Then it came to me; why aren't I doing more of this on my own?

"I still find it a challenge to practise every day. I will do a short practice first thing in the morning and then before bed. But I can always get to mindful moments throughout the day. When I ride my bike to work, I try to do mindful practice throughout the ride. I'll also try for a longer twenty- to thirty-minute sit several times a week, but I don't always get to that.

"Little reminders are really helpful. I found a beautiful little heart-shaped stone one day that now sits beside my computer. It's a reminder to me; when I get wound up or panicky, just take a second and breathe, let it flow through me. It's little things like that throughout the day that have made the biggest impact."

What has been the impact on your life?

"I've noticed really big changes, mostly in my relationship with myself. I'm more aware of my inner narrator that always used to make me think twice about everything. Now I just relax, break it down into its component parts and it fades away on its own. I have also learned to check in to my body when I'm feeling tense. What is the sensation in my gut, chest or head? Then I can breathe through it and let it go. I've always been an anxious person; I was even told I should be entered into a clinical trial for medication. Personally, I don't want to go there; meditation has been the best technique for me.

"Awareness is the first step in breaking any bad habit—like my eating challenges. When you can check in to what you're feeling and why, it takes away from those automatic responses.

"I've spent the last ten years living on a merry-go-round. Now my friends and family say that I've slowed down; I'm less stressed out and more grounded. My relationships have all improved. And I can enjoy little moments a lot more. Instead of being cranky while I'm standing in line at the grocery checkout,

I can share a smile with the person next to me or admire the beautiful vegetables. My life feels a lot richer."

What advice would you give to others?
"For me community support has been really important. When friends want to try it, I tell them not to put pressure on themselves to feel a certain way. Everyone has different experiences. It's like exercising; you're not going to run a marathon tomorrow. If you start working toward a steady pace, you will see the benefits. You may have the most painful forty-five minutes of your life; you may not feel the benefits until later in the week. Stay open-minded. Try many different techniques and use the one that works for you."

DIFFERENT PEOPLE, different challenges. What could be going on to enable such a range of outcomes? For some, it was the release of emotional baggage, whether from life circumstances, life choices or vicarious trauma. For some, it was finding ways to cope with physical discomfort or extreme pain. Some found a deep source of steadiness or peace underneath the waves of surface upheavals. What is going on in the brain, body and mind that such a simple intervention could lead to a range of powerful outcomes? That is what we will explore in the next two chapters.

[3]

Changes to Brain and Body

MEDITATION TECHNIQUES of various kinds are not new. They have been practised for thousands of years around the world, typically by monks or nuns as part of their contemplative life. What is new is the number of people practising modern versions of traditional techniques, as are scientific studies on the impact of meditation on these people. These studies are made possible by advances in neuroscience, including measurement devices such as the fMRI and EEG. The number of mindfulness studies published in journals has exploded from virtually none in 1980 to 674 in 2015, with the number of peer-reviewed research publications almost identical at 661.[7]

Acknowledgement must go to the pioneering work of Dr. Jon Kabat-Zinn,[8] creator of the Mindfulness-Based Stress Reduction program. He was the first to develop a secular program based on several meditation techniques but freed of dogmatic content. He originally introduced it in clinical settings for individuals suffering from chronic pain or stress-related disorders. The Mindfulness-Based Stress Reduction Clinic at the University of Massachusetts Medical School initiated some of the first clinical studies.

The first generation of studies established the credibility of mindfulness. But they were limited by what were of necessity small sample sizes and sometimes unrepresentative subjects, such as Buddhist monks who spent hours every day in meditation. Newer, second-generation studies are addressing these challenges through improved research methodologies that include randomized studies and placebo control groups. We are now at the stage where there is sufficient credibility for mindfulness, such that the Mindfulness All-Party Parliamentary Group in the UK can confidently state that "mindfulness has a role to play in tackling our mental health crisis, where one in three families includes someone who is mentally ill." [9] What is the science telling us?

Rewires the Brain for Focus and Happiness

We know that the brain changes its structure as a result of experience all the time. Called neuroplasticity, this capacity for change in neuronal patterns occurs in response to a variety of stimuli, from the navigational knowledge that London taxi drivers must acquire to learning a new motor task like juggling to meditation practice. Mindfulness has been shown to produce measurable structural and functional changes in the brain. Areas of the brain associated with mind wandering, stress and anxiety are less active; areas of the brain associated with cognitive control and positive mood are increased:

- A study at Yale University found that mindfulness practices decreases activity in the brain network responsible for mind wandering and self-referential thoughts. Sometimes called the "me centre" or "default mode network," this area is active when we're not intentionally thinking about anything in particular. Activation in this default mode network (or "default attentional network") is typically associated with being less happy, ruminating and worrying about the past or future.[10]

- Sarah Lazar and her team at Harvard demonstrated that eight weeks of mindfulness training increased cortical thickness in the hippocampus, an area of the brain that governs learning and memory, and also in areas of the brain that play roles in emotional regulation and self-referential processing. They also found decreases in brain cell volume in the amygdala, the part of the brain implicated in processing fear, anxiety and the responses to stress. Participants reported feeling less stressed after the training program. A follow-up study indicated that changes in brain areas linked to mood and arousal were associated with improvements in reported well-being.[11]

- A central claim of mindfulness is that it improves concentration and focus. Cognitive neuroscientist Dr. Michael Mrazek of the University of California, Santa Barbara, has corroborated this. A few weeks of mindfulness practice improved focus and memory equivalent to sixteen percentile points during the verbal reasoning portion of the GRE (graduate and business school test).[12]

Some studies focus on longer-term impacts:

- A UCLA study found that the brains of long-term meditators experienced a diminished reduction in grey matter in regions throughout the brain, suggesting that mindfulness may offset cortical thinning brought on by aging.[13]

- Dr. Richard Davidson of the University of Wisconsin–Madison has demonstrated that long-term meditators show changes in the neural circuits involved in resilience, experiencing a speedier recovery from amygdala arousal. (Caution: This can take six to seven thousand hours of practice.)[14]

Some newer studies are comparing the effects of mindfulness meditation with a placebo:

- In January 2016, Carnegie Mellon gave thirty-five unemployed men and women three days of intensive training. Half practised mindfulness meditation at a retreat centre for three days; the other half spent three days engaged in relaxation training. At the end of three days, everyone said they felt less stressed, but follow-up brain scans showed differences only in those who underwent mindfulness meditation. Four months later, those who had practised mindfulness showed lower levels in their blood of a marker of unhealthy inflammation than the relaxation group, even though few were still meditating.[15]

Reduces Stress and Improves Well-Being

Numerous studies have found that mindfulness practice can have a significant positive effect on factors of well-being, including stress, pain, negative mood and anxiety. Many clinicians are now recommending that mindfulness practice be included as a viable option in treatment programs:

- A Johns Hopkins study found that mindfulness meditation reduced the symptoms of depression, anxiety and pain at a moderate rate, equivalent to antidepressants.[16]

- A Boston University meta-analysis found significant effects on patients diagnosed with anxiety and mood disorders, with a moderate effect produced for a larger sample size.[17]

- A meta-analysis of multiple mindfulness studies published in 2014 in *JAMA* (the *Journal of the American Medical Association*) found that meditation programs can result in small to moderate reduction in multiple negative dimensions of psychological stress, such as anxiety, depression and pain.[18]

- Mindfulness-Based Cognitive Therapy (MBCT)—mindfulness practice in conjunction with Cognitive Behavioural Therapy—has been shown to be effective in preventing relapse in recurrent depression, so effective that the "Mindful Nation UK" report recommends that MBCT be made available to individuals at risk of recurrent depression through the National Health Service.[19]

- A study published in the November 2014 edition of the journal *Pain Medicine* found that two years after completing MBSR training, participants were significantly better at accepting and managing chronic pain and seemed to have more vitality.[20]

- As reported by the UCLA Mindful Awareness Research Center, a 2007 study showed that after only five days of meditation training at twenty minutes a day, students reported less anxiety, depression and anger compared to a group of students that received relaxation training.[21]

Fosters Empathy and Positive Relationships

Mindfulness instructions always encourage an attitude of curiosity and kindness. Sometimes specific practices are used to intentionally nurture positive outcomes. These appear to have an impact both on our brains and on how we actually behave:

- A 2008 study showed that longer-term meditators had more activation in those areas of the brain that detect emotional cues, demonstrating heightened empathic awareness.[22]

- As referenced in the online learning site Headspace, a 2013 study found that people who practised mindfulness for eight weeks displayed a fifty percent increase in compassionate behaviours in real life settings, compared to those who did not meditate.[23]

- As referenced in Headspace, a 2008 study found that the increased self-awareness and non-judgmental acceptance associated with mindfulness leads to better communications of feelings and reduced social anxiety.[24]

What can we conclude from the physiological studies? We know that mindfulness produces verifiable, measurable changes in the brain and to markers of stress. We don't know enough to prescribe mindfulness as precisely as we would a pill or a drug. For many people, knowing about these physiological effects makes mindfulness real, justifying the effort involved. However, when you are practising mindfulness, you do not feel the brain rewiring itself. You do become aware of psychological changes in your perceptions and emotions. Let's look at those now.

[4]

Building the Muscles of Resilience

<hr>

THE ORDINARY heroes you met in Chapter 2 all found that mindfulness helped them to cope, enabling them to live more fulfilling lives. They had developed resilience in the face of stress or trauma.

Stress is an external force or change that requires an adjustment or response from us, whether that adjustment is physical, mental or emotional. So stress is a normal part of life. Our bodies are designed to experience stress and react to it. It can keep us alert, ready to avoid danger or to take on new challenges. Stress can become negative when we experience it continuously, without periods of rest or relaxation in between. Without relief, continuous stress becomes distress. Distress costs each of us, whether physically or psychologically. Stress can play a part in headaches, high blood pressure, heart problems, diabetes, skin conditions, asthma, arthritis, depression and anxiety. Stress costs all of us societally. It has been estimated that stress costs American industry more than $300 billion annually.

Why do different people respond to similar stresses quite differently? Part of the answer lies in our own personal resilience. This ability to bounce back can make the difference between experiencing normal stress that encourages our growth and distress that renders us stuck or overwhelmed. How do we get to be the kind of person who, after an initial devastation or loss, can say, "It may have been the best thing that ever happened to me"?

Resilience is the ability to recover, adapt and grow in response to threat or challenge.

Resilience is a complex concept. It involves external factors, such as social supports from our friends and families, as well as our own internal resources. These internal resources are based both on inborn traits and on abilities we can develop. So while you may have been born with an optimistic temperament (lucky you), resilience is a capacity you can actively foster. Resilient people do experience negative emotions and stress; but they have learned to navigate around and through crises. How do they do that? What are the capabilities they have developed in order to become more resilient?

Just as muscles are composed of strands of fibres, so the capacity for resilience is composed of competencies and abilities. Based on my coaching training and meditation experience, I am going to propose seven such competencies. Let's refer to these as the seven muscles of resilience. These competencies are based on well-accepted resilience assessment instruments [25] and on research evidence from the fields of adult development and personal change processes. Taken together, these muscles of resilience form a robust model of the internal resources that we can grow within us to become more resilient. What do these seven muscles of resilience have to do with mindfulness?

Mindfulness as a Resilience Booster

What I want to suggest—and hope to demonstrate in the next few pages—is that mindfulness practice can support growth in each of these muscles of resilience. Mindfulness works like a vaccine that supports resilience for the mind and emotions. Medical vaccines build physical resilience by inserting a small, safe dosage of what otherwise might be harmful into the body, stimulating the immune system so that the body can ward off disease. Now I know that some people question the efficacy or safety of vaccines. While it is important to be aware of and address the potential side effects of vaccinations, widespread vaccination programs have led to vastly improved health outcomes that many of us now take for granted. Only access to clean water, which the World Health Organization considers to be a basic human right, has done more for our physical health than have vaccinations against infectious diseases.

Mindfulness works along similar principles to a vaccine. You undertake practices that can initially feel odd or counterintuitive. You practise in safe, low-risk ways. In doing so, you stimulate the natural recovery and growth mechanisms of the human mind and emotions. Resilience muscles that you build while meditating become strong enough to kick in naturally in daily life, when the stakes are high and you need them the most. Mindfulness, too, can have side effects, which is why managed doses, sound instruction and occasional touch points with a competent coach are helpful.

Here are, in my view, the seven muscles of resilience and information about how mindfulness practice can help you build them. The first five muscles support your ability to recover more quickly in the face of stress or trauma. The last two muscles support your ability to adapt and grow in response to challenges.

Resilience Muscles for Recovery

Let's use basic instructions for mindfulness of the breath to explore how this works. While the breath method is by no means the only way to practise mindfulness—in Chapters 7 to 9 I will introduce you to several more—the basic principles remain the same:

"Focus your awareness on your breath, staying attentive to the sensations of inhalation and exhalation, and start again at the next breath. Do not judge your breathing or try to change it in any way. See anything else that comes to mind as a distraction; let distractions go and return your attention to the breath."[26]

Resilience Muscle #1:
Ability to Persist Through Obstacles or Failures

After experiencing a setback, a resilient person is able to try again. This ability to persist is a core measure of resilience on psychological tests. We also appreciate the value of persistence in everyday sayings. "When you fall off a horse, get back on." Or, "Success consists of getting back up just one more time than you fall down." The capacity for perseverance is in part a heritable trait that we are born with. And we can learn to enhance our innate capacities, whether through practising persistence itself or developing its enabling factors, such as staying focused under pressure, handling difficult feelings or developing a greater sense of personal control.

Learning mindfulness involves continuous practice in persistence. Once you focus your attention on something (the breath, the body), you *will* be distracted. Guaranteed! That's why the instructions specifically refer to this: "See anything else that comes to mind as a distraction; let distractions go and return your attention to the breath." What do you do when your attention wanders? Just bring it back, over and over again. Each time you return your attention to the chosen object of focus, you exercise the muscle of persistence. With practice, this returning gets easier. Slowly, you learn to interpret distraction not as a failure of attention but as an opportunity to experience success in persistence. Persistence becomes something you can trust.

Resilience Muscle #2:
Ability to Stay Focused Under Pressure

When faced with a challenge, a resilient person is able to stay focused on the task at hand. We have all faced high-pressure moments, whether a looming deadline, too much to do in the time available, a big game or an important meeting. We may know what we want to do, but we can also experience anxiety, doubts, fears or physical tensions. These worries and tensions can be so strong that they overwhelm us. Like waves washing over the side of a small boat, we feel swamped; we are no longer able to retain our focus. We "lose our nerve" and don't perform to the best of our ability. At moments like these, we are actually not capable of applying all the resources and skills that we have.

Mindfulness practice involves repeated acts of focus. Just look at the first words of the instructions. "Focus your awareness on the breath ... Start again at the next breath." One of the core skills you build in mindfulness is concentration. You learn that your attention doesn't just happen. It is a faculty that you can intentionally direct, as you choose. This choice of focus can be as narrow as the breath at the tip of your nose or as wide as all your sensory experience. In mindfulness practice, you learn the ability to stay focused on what you deem is relevant at any given time, when you're not under pressure, so that you can stay focused when you need it in the pressures of daily life.

Resilience Muscle #3:
Ability to Handle Unpleasant Feelings

When you are faced with a threat or challenge, your primal emotions are going to kick in. The question is, how will your emotions affect your behaviour? A resilient person will be able to experience even very strong emotions, without unduly driving or distorting their actions. Our emotions are wired deep in the limbic system of our brains. Here the amygdala performs an essential function for survival, acting as the brain's radar for danger and triggering the fight-or-flight response. When the amygdala activates, it hijacks the brain's executive centres in the prefrontal cortex. One neural measure of resilience is the speed with which the amygdala recovers from this state of heightened arousal. (Earlier, we saw that long-term meditators are able to recover more quickly from this kind of "amygdala hijack.") It's not just strong emotions in response to major threats that can derail us. We may not be fully in touch with our everyday emotions. You may have been raised not to show certain emotions. (I was.) Or you may be afraid that if you allow yourself to feel the full force of your emotions, you will explode with rage, implode with despair or act in a way that you later regret. So you keep a lid on it.

Emotional intelligence is the ability to identify and manage your emotions and the emotions of others. The first skill in emotional intelligence is being aware of your emotions, able to identify and name them. Resilient people have high emotional intelligence. They are able to sit with strong emotions—theirs and others'—knowing that emotions ebb and flow naturally, of their own accord. They are able to readily name their emotions, can often point to parts of the body where these emotions are experienced and can identify their specific triggers. (When someone is critical of me, I get angry and feel it in the tension in my jaw.)

Mindfulness practice helps you develop emotional intelligence in several ways. First, you learn to develop a non-judgmental attitude toward what you are experiencing. Look at the second line of the instructions: "Do not judge your breathing or try to change it in any way." This accepting attitude helps you develop the skill of equanimity, neither pushing away nor holding on to whatever you are experiencing. Equanimity can be applied to anything, including the emotions you may be feeling while you're meditating. So if you are feeling angry, you don't judge yourself for feeling anger. You don't push away (or hang on to) the emotion of anger. Equanimity is the key to dialling down the intensity—but not the reality—of your feelings. When you can experience your emotions directly, without suppressing, denying or amplifying them, you experience them as they actually are.

Mindfulness—in particular the clear sensory distinctions encouraged by Unified Mindfulness—helps you disentangle complex emotions. What we call a feeling has several components: physical sensations in the body and the mental stories with which you interpret them. Normally, we experience these all at once, bundled up together, with no separation among the various strands. When you can disentangle the separate strands (there's the physical sensation, there's the mental talk) you are less likely to be overwhelmed by your emotions. It's like trying to unsnarl a large knot: At first, it seems impossible, but when you become aware of the separate strands and gently, persistently work them, eventually they loosen and the knot unravels. The emotions you experience during mindfulness practice will often be quite ordinary. But as you develop facility in processing ordinary emotions, you are much more prepared to handle the strong emotions that come from prolonged stress, significant challenge or even trauma.

Resilience Muscle #4:
Ability to Stay Connected with Others

No one is able to be resilient all by themselves. A strong social network of friends, family or neighbours who can support us when the chips are down is an essential component of resilience. Unfortunately, too many of us do not reach out to others when we're stretched. Perhaps we are unwilling to express our vulnerability, or we may be so overwhelmed that we do not recognize the subtle cues of support being offered to us.

How can mindfulness, which is often (but not necessarily) practised by yourself, help you connect better to other people? I think there are several ways. When you are meditating, focused on your breath (or whatever you have chosen to focus on), you become very aware of many other things that are not your breath. Other body sensations, mental chatter, other sounds around you. From one perspective, these are distractions. Your ability to stay focused (resilience muscle #2) and to persist in your efforts (resilience muscle #1) are important. From another perspective, sensations, chatter, sounds and so on are insights. This is who you are. These physical sensations and inner chatter are you. You come face to face with whatever is going on inside you: the good, the bad and the ugly. Through mindfulness practice you become more aware and accepting of your vulnerabilities and weaknesses, so in real life you're less embarrassed by yourself, more likely to reach out to others when you need it.

Mindfulness can also deliberately include compassion practices, with which you intentionally cultivate good will toward others and yourself. The very fact that these practices can at first feel so awkward indicates how unaccustomed we are to developing new kinds of connections with others. Practising new kinds of connections in an interior way means we are more capable of doing this in an exterior, "real" way when the need arises.

Resilience Muscle #5: Sense of Self-Efficacy

A resilient person thinks differently than others. Less resilient people will perceive challenges as pervasive and permanent and accordingly feel a sense of helplessness. More resilient people are likely to think of a challenge as a specific, potentially changeable part of their life, over which they have some control. They have a sense of self-efficacy. They believe that control or influence resides in themselves, not solely in their environment. With this belief, they are more likely to respond to a challenge as a chance to grow versus as an overwhelming trauma. The cognitive skill of perception—the view that challenge is something that you can control and master—is a key underpinning of resilience. These beliefs and self-perceptions affect our actual behaviours. If you believe that a challenge, while difficult, may be an opportunity to grow, you are more likely to stretch yourself, try out new behaviours and, through practice, achieve new kinds of mastery. People who have a sense of self-efficacy report experiencing less stress and performing better.

Unfortunately, like a self-fulfilling prophecy, these cognitive skills can work both ways. You can also exaggerate stressors in your mind, worry and ruminate, creating a mountain out of a molehill. Says George Bonanno, who studies resilience at the Loss, Trauma and Emotion Lab of Columbia University's Teachers College, "Frame adversity as a challenge, and you become more flexible and able to deal with it, move and learn from it, and grow. Focus on it, frame it as a threat and a potentially traumatic event becomes an enduring problem; you become more inflexible and more likely to be negatively affected."[27]

Mindfulness skills affect our sense of self-efficacy in two ways: through an awareness of continuous change and through an approach versus avoidance strategy to risk.

In mindfulness practice, when you focus your attention on something, you quickly become aware of how much things are constantly changing. Each of your breaths has a beginning and an ending. Your body sensations come and go. Your thoughts and feelings come in bursts or waves. At first, this might feel odd or scary. With exposure you become accustomed to an inner fluidity. Movement not fixedness becomes the new normal. Your assumptions about permanence and change have subtly shifted. So when a difficult challenge arises in your life, you are less likely to automatically assume it is permanent, more likely to view it as temporary.

When your assumptions about permanence and change shift, your built-in tendencies in how to approach challenge also shift. If you assume that threats are permanent, you are more likely to brace against them, fight or flee them. If you assume that threats are temporary, you are more likely to turn toward them, inquire and become curious about them. Our usual response to threats is natural, based on millennia of wiring for survival. We brace ourselves for potential threat, preparing ourselves to fight or flee from a dangerous predator. This instantaneous response is effective in the face of physical danger but also shuts down potential new learning.

With mindfulness practice, you become exquisitely aware of where and how this internal bracing is occurring in you, whether in physical tensions or emotionally hardened attitudes. You learn to relax and open toward these experiences rather than automatically tighten around them. When you are not automatically tightening and turning away from experiences, you have a chance to develop curiosity, a prerequisite for learning. Mindfulness can help develop this attitude of curiosity and inquiry. When you bring curiosity and inquiry into real life, you are more likely to detect subtle cues in what's going on in your environment. You notice things you would have previously missed. You find yourself responding more effectively to challenges. Researchers such as Daniel Siegel[28] and Mark Epstein[29] also surmise that a fundamental mechanism in mindfulness practice is the skill of turning toward experience with an attitude of curiosity and learning instead of an automatic response of bracing against potential threats to survival.

When you become more comfortable with continuous change, you sense that there is one thing that is not changing. That is the "you" witnessing all these changing experiences. This witnessing "you" comes from a deeper place; it feels steadier. As you become accustomed to this interior, steadier "you," you more naturally respond from this place. When stresses hit you, you are more able to give a considered response rather than an instinctive, shoot-from-the-hip reaction. Your locus of control has shifted to a deeper bedrock.

Resilience Muscles for Adaptation and Growth

Remember our definition of resilience? "Resilience is the ability to recover, adapt and grow in response to threat or challenge." The first five muscles help you through the recovery phase: persist through obstacles, stay focused under pressure, handle unpleasant feelings, stay connected to others and develop self-efficacy. Once you have recovered, you have the opportunity to adapt and grow. You can learn to solve new kinds of problems or solve old problems in new ways. For this we turn to two further muscles of resilience. Helping clients develop these muscles is a foundational piece to my coaching approach.

Resilience Muscle #6:
Looking *At* Versus Looking *Through*

Resilient people don't just stubbornly persist through challenges. Failure can teach them that they need to solve problems in new ways. But first they have to be aware of their current way of solving problems. Most of us are blind to this. In the Integral Coaching Method®, developed by Joanne Hunt and Laura Divine, they call this your Current Way of Being. "When we live from certain ways of seeing and going in the world, we are unaware that we are operating from these places/assumptions. They are simply 'me.' We are blind to our Current Way of Being, operating on automatic pilot and governed by unknown assumptions."[30]

Here's an example: I wear contact lenses. Let's imagine I have permanent lenses that are slightly grey in colour. Since I always wear them, I don't know that the lenses are grey. I look at the world, see it as a rather dark place and act accordingly. Then one day, I notice I am wearing lenses. I take them off. Suddenly, the world looks different. I see that the grey was my perception of the world, not the way the world is. I am able to look *at* my perception ("grey-ness") instead of *through* it.

As developed by Hunt and Divine, this ability to look *at* our assumptions and not look *through* them offers significant opportunities for effective adaptation to challenges. Robert Kegan at the Harvard Graduate School of Education also calls this "the subject-object shift." It is a natural, fundamental process that undergirds our growing-up process from infancy to adolescence into mature adulthood. As Kegan notes, "An object refers to any element of our knowing that we can reflect on, look at, handle, be responsible for, relate to. Subject refers to those elements of our knowing that we are identified with, tied to, fused with or embedded in. We *have* object; we *are* subject."[31]

When we can perceive an aspect of our experience, we can take responsibility and problem solve for it. When we are identified or fused with something, we cannot even see it. We are subject to it. To continue with the example above, at first I am looking *through* my grey contact lenses. Unconsciously. I am subject to grey-ness and behave accordingly. I develop a slightly pessimistic mood. When I look *at* my slightly grey assumptions, I can disidentify from them. I see they may not necessarily be true. I can begin to test my assumptions and act differently. I could ask others if they see a situation the same way I do. I could deliberately hang out with those of a more optimistic nature.

Mindfulness initiates this process of healthy disidentification, or the subject-object move within us. It enables us to look *at* what we were formerly looking *through*. No matter what you choose to focus on during your mindfulness practice—the breath or your sensations of feeling, seeing or hearing—you will become aware of thoughts and feelings you didn't know you had. You see, often for the first time, what you are actually thinking and feeling in real time. This is a very powerful experience. When you were not aware of these thoughts and feelings, you were looking *through* them. They became the basis for unexamined assumptions about you and the world around you. Now, for the first time, you can look *at* them. The part of you that is aware of what you are thinking or feeling is not the part that is thinking or feeling. The contents of what you are thinking and feeling have now become object to a larger you that is the new subject. This larger you creates a wider space within which feelings and sensations can come and go more freely, with less friction. This may underlie the phenomenon of spaciousness or lightness that many meditators experience. (I have experienced this as greater ease of physical movement or more humour with contentious emotions or less need to be always right!)

When you are able to look *at* what you were formerly looking *through*, you can now take responsibility for it. You have a freedom not previously available to you. You can choose to act in new ways. Without this freedom, you are unconsciously chained to your old ways. When you are practising mindfulness, in some ways, it doesn't really matter what you are experiencing. It could be pleasant thoughts or unpleasant feelings. What does matter is that by becoming aware of these thoughts and feelings, you are now able to disidentify from what were previously unconscious patterns in a healthy, non-threatening way. You are developing a larger you that can look at and test assumptions you didn't even know you were making. This ability to look *at* versus look *through* is an essential first step in the process of personal change, which we'll look at next.

Resilience Muscle #7: Process of Personal Change

While the process of personal change is rarely painless, resilient people are able to move through it with relative ease. They are able to leverage shocks as signals for change, recognize that something is no longer working for them and explore new options. They become more comfortable with the process of shedding an old identity and creating a new one.

The content and pacing of each transition is unique, but the process itself follows a predictable sequence. As an Integral

Master Coach™, I am familiar with the concepts from many models of personal change, but here I'll use Otto Scharmer's U curve as a representative model.[32] The process has three broad phases: letting go of the old, allowing a gap or transition and letting come something new.

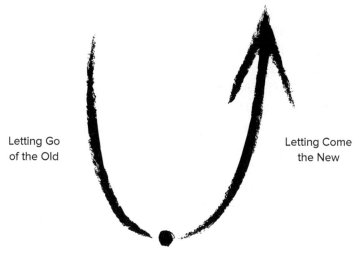

Letting Go
of the Old

Letting Come
the New

Gap of Transition

For much of our lives, we are not in transition. (Good thing; it can be exhausting!) We are in performance mode, our behaviour and thinking in well-honed grooves of habit. We are reasonably effective in our lives. Our habit patterns serve us well, so we don't have to think too much about them. We are operating on automatic pilot.

Then some kind of setback, challenge or trauma occurs. We respond in our usual ways but find they don't work very well anymore. This precipitates the transition process, starting at the upper left side of the U curve. We saw this with Nicola's divorce, Alex's PTSD and Barbara's business setback in Chapter 2.

The left side of the curve is the letting go phase. It is all about unlearning old habits, disidentifying from your current sense of self. You start the process by hitting the pause button, in effect suspending your automatic ways of being and doing. You redirect awareness to observe yourself, others and your situation more deeply. You start to become conscious of things you did unconsciously. You can now look *at* what you used to look *through* (resilience muscle #6). When you are able to do this thoroughly, you can let go of the old.

But you do not immediately jump into the new, even though you may want to. The bottom of the U curve is the gap of transition. It is an awkward in-between zone, the gap between your old self and your new self, where you are neither one thing nor another. You have disidentified from your old self, but haven't yet found a new one. The bottom of the U is a place of questions but not yet answers, where you rest in the unknown. What do you really want? What does the situation truly call for? What gives you energy and joy? Who do you truly care for? Because you have let go of old patterns, you are able to see with fresh eyes. Eventually you detect the glimmering of new answers to your questions, which precipitates the right-hand side of the U curve. The unknown is the place where possibilities exist. The unknown is the only place from which you can truly create the new.

The right-hand side of the U is about letting come something fresh and new. You construct a newer identity, you figure out more effective ways of doing and being that respond to your deeper longings. Because you have let go of old ways, you are able to let come that which is truly innovative. You are able to tap into a creativity you may not have suspected. These new possibilities emerge at first in small whispers. You try out new moves in tentative, low-risk "pilot project" ways. You learn from your first mistakes and eventually crystallize those moves into effective new ways. When you are able to embody these new ways on a consistent basis, they have become embodied in you. You have a new set of habits, more effective and personally fulfilling than before. You have enacted the new.

To illustrate, let's use the analogy of a caterpillar turning into a butterfly. Before any kind of transition occurs, we are like the caterpillar, happily munching away, feeding ourselves, growing in our lives. Then a signal for change hits. The caterpillar stops eating, stops moving and attaches itself to a twig or leaf. It constructs a protective cocoon around itself and turns inward. Inside that protective cocoon, it literally dissolves. Its formerly solid body turns into a rich gooey fluid, which contains the embryonic cells for its new form. When the protective cocoon is no longer needed, it is shed and the new creature—a butterfly—emerges.

What has this process of personal change got to do with mindfulness? Without perhaps realizing it, people practising mindfulness methods mimic and can catalyze a process of personal change. All mindfulness methods can initiate the left-hand, letting go side of the U curve. They enable us to look *at* and thereby disidentify from our usual unconscious patterns. We redirect our awareness in new ways.

Shinzen Young's Unified Mindfulness is unique in offering practices that address all three phases of the U curve change process: Appreciate Self and World practices help you see beyond your automatic patterns, thereby letting go of the old; Transcend Self and World practices let you touch deeply into the space of transition; Nurture Positive in Self and World practices help you let come something new (see Chapter 6).

Why would you want all these practices? Because resilience, change and personal growth are multi-faceted and messy. At different times, you may need different tools. An integrated suite of techniques provides a balanced approach to psycho-spiritual development, addressing the risks of one-sided development. If you practise only on the left side of the U curve, deconstructing and letting go of your old self, you may become more vividly aware of and in tune with yourself and the world around you, but you risk becoming narcissistic or disengaged. If you practise only at the bottom of the U, resting in the unknown, you may be in touch with the deepest source of love and truth, but you risk not actively embodying it or bringing those values into the world. If you practise only the right-hand side of the U, reconstructing a better you, you may move toward your ideals, but you do so in a shallow way. You risk a naïve idealism that quickly smashes against the hard rocks of reality, either burning out or not being able to walk your talk. Think of it like filling a glass with a fine wine. First you have to empty out the old wine and clean the glass (let go), then leave the glass empty while the wine breathes in its bottle (gap of transition), then slowly pour in the fine new wine (let come).

With these seven muscles of resilience in mind, you can appreciate that mindfulness practice may be simple, yet it is powerful. It's like the TARDIS space-time vehicle on my husband's favourite TV show, *Dr. Who*: small on the outside, bigger on the inside. With this context now set, let's turn to practical matters—your capacity to deeply pay attention.

[5]

Mindfulness as Attentional Transformation

COULD YOU tell me about what you do for a living? Can you describe what sort of person you are? Of course you can. You do it all the time, when meeting new people or talking with friends. But can you describe how you pay attention? Probably not. Yet you are paying attention all the time. You rely on the capacity for attention unconsciously, like an unknown, untapped resource.

Your physical capacities, such as stamina or flexibility, can be compared to your attentional capacities. We all rely on our bodies unconsciously every day, yet they are not just a given. Our inherent capacities can be enhanced with training. Our bodies also reflect our way of living. Physical labour is hard on the body. Smoking affects the lungs. Prolonged sitting for most of the day can lead to organ damage, muscle degeneration or weight gain.

Similarly, we rely on our attention all the time. It is not just a given. With training, we can enhance our capacity to pay attention. Where and how we pay attention also reflects habitual patterns and preconceptions. We may see the world not as it is but as we are.

Mindfulness develops your capacity to pay attention. Just as exercise can enhance your physical health, so mindfulness can transform your mental health, tapping into a resource you didn't know you had, elevating the baseline from which you live your life. Physical exercise trains your body to be strong, flexible and fit; mindfulness trains your mental muscles to be focused, clear and equanimous.

Your Two Selves

Exciting new developments in neuroscience are pointing to what psychologists and spiritual teachers have long suspected. We have multiple "selves" within us.

As we saw in the science review section of Chapter 3, specific regions of the prefrontal cortex are associated with what is called the default mode network, or the default attentional network. This area of the brain is active when we are not intentionally thinking about anything in particular, like a default setting humming along quietly in the background. It may correlate with our lived experience of a stable, coherent sense of self. This sense of self is based on our experiences built up over time. We develop core-beliefs systems and narratives to interpret our experiences. I will affectionately refer to this stable part of ourselves as DAN (short for default attentional network).

But DAN does not operate alone. There is another part of our brain that processes the moment-by-moment sensations that indicate changes in our exterior environment or in ourselves. Dr. Norman Farb at the University of Toronto has demonstrated that mindful awareness training tunes this region of the brain, called the posterior insula.[33] Let's call this area MoMo, short for moment-by-moment awareness. In contrast to DAN, MoMo is concerned with what is happening in the present moment of now; every moment of now, over and over. (These two selves may be analogous to the experiencing self and remembering self of Daniel Kahneman, popularized in his book *Thinking, Fast and Slow*.[34])

Usually, moment-by-moment changes are not significant, so MoMo hums along quietly in the background, like an invisible workhorse. We literally do not see (or hear) subtle changes in our environment, as we don't need to. But sometimes there are significant changes or emergencies, like an angry boss, a crying baby or a vehicle cutting in front of us. Then MoMo naturally leaps from the background to the foreground. We become acutely aware of momentary sensations: the look on a face, a tone of voice, how quickly we need to brake the car.

Mindfulness training tunes up the posterior insula. The good news is that you can develop capacities for higher levels of detection and even bandwidth in moment-by-moment sensing. This enhanced capacity enables you to approach stale information with fresh eyes, the beginner's mind you may have heard about. It is this greater freshness that is behind all novelty, change and creativity. When you engage in mindfulness training, you are bypassing your standard attentional processing patterns, hacking into DAN to pay greater attention to moment-by-moment sensory experiences. The bad news is that, at first, mindfulness training can feel awkward or counterintuitive, like swimming against a strong current.

Effective mindfulness practices integrate both MoMo and DAN: our capacities for attention in the now and our intention for how we apply these capacities going forward. By developing greater moment-by-moment awareness, we tap in to new possibilities. By integrating this awareness with positive intentions, we alter both our sense of who we are and how we are able to function in the world.

Like any other training, developing mindful awareness is a process. Your first learning moment—which perhaps you are experiencing right now—is that attention and intention are not static givens but dynamic capabilities. When you begin to practise, these muscles are weak. You become aware that your current state of attention is usually fragmented, superficial, reacting automatically to thoughts and events. With time and practice, these mental muscles become stronger. They become permanently elevated, not just when you are practising, but throughout your daily life. You find yourself reacting habitually less often (DAN), noticing what is happening in the present moment more often (MoMo) and responding more effectively from a heightened awareness.

For example, let's say I was the lead on a project team approaching an important milestone. Someone from the client group presents me with a last-minute change. My habitual response would be to keep the client happy, put my head down, drive myself and others too hard, then go home and complain. With greater mindful awareness, I might notice the tension in my body, a feeling of panic, the apologetic look on the client's face. Then I might be more able to engage in a productive dialogue about requirements and timelines.

As you become more resilient in dealing with challenges and more effective in daily life, you spend less time and energy in dealing with the same old issues. You get in your own way less and less. This frees up your inner potential to emerge, both in terms of your unique individual talents and broader human potentials, such as joy, peace and love. You are able to direct more energy into goals and values that are personally meaningful. Your consciousness enters a heightened state of meta-awareness that is calmer, broader, deeper and more all-encompassing. Your capacity for heightened awareness has transformed your life.

But this transformation doesn't happen overnight. Like any skill or capacity, you need to invest some time and energy into practice. There is a learning curve to navigate. You can picture this as a modified version of the "J" curve often found in the field of organizational change. I have adapted this to mindfulness practice. You start off eager and motivated. You may experience tastes of calm and lightness. Then you hit the valley of the J curve. Your first steps are wobbly. You become aware—painfully, for the first time—of how chaotic or driven your thoughts and inner states really are. Hacking into DAN can feel strenuous. You start with good intentions for regular practice, but because your first experiences may be wobbly or awkward, you find yourself slipping on your commitments. The practices and guidelines in this book are meant to help you understand and navigate your way through the challenges of the J curve, emerging on the other side with consistently stronger mindful awareness both when you are practising and in daily life.

Skill building means repetition; there are no shortcuts here. But there is smart practice. Like any skill, you start with basic knowledge of what's involved and a motivation for change. Then you learn a few key instructions and apply them in meaningful ways in your life. This enables you to review your practice, assess where you are experiencing some benefits and where you still have challenges. Then you can repeat the cycle, finding ways to extend your practice and judiciously push your edge. The content of this book follows this sequence. First, I give you the basic knowledge and help anchor your motivation, then provide a range of methods and lastly help you find ways to integrate practice in your life.

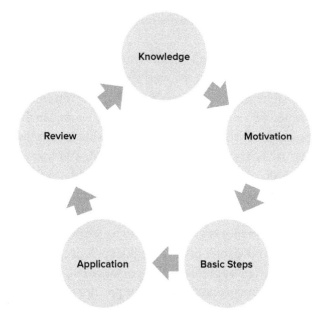

For example, when I first started exercising, I went to a weekly Pilates class, both to learn the basic moves and to be motivated by practising with others. At first, I was exhausted. Everyone was doing so many more repetitions than I was; they made it look easy! I felt like I could never do this. But gradually new muscles developed. I felt stronger and could do the moves both more often and with more precision. I wanted to extend the practice but just didn't have the time to go to classes more frequently. So I found ways to apply the moves in daily life, like brushing my teeth while standing on one leg!

The Challenges

Meditation techniques can be simple to understand. What may not be easy is the personal change needed to develop a sustainable mindfulness habit, carving out the new neural pathways that enhance MoMo and navigate around DAN. As we saw in Chapter 2, roughly one in ten people who takes a mindfulness course is practising regularly one year later. My hope with this book is for you personally to beat these odds and for all of us together to change the playing field so that anyone who wants to can be successful.

As I see it, there are five main challenges in developing a sustainable mindfulness practice. The first four are part of any personal change effort; only the last one is unique to meditation:

1   Why should I bother? You need to have a compelling reason to try something new: both a sense of what future success might look like and the current stresses or suffering that are driving you to change. Later in this chapter, I will help you articulate your motivation for practice. A Mindfulness Topic Statement will guide and support you in the early, wobbly stage of the J curve.

2   How do I do the practice? Once you have landed on the "why" of motivation, you need the "how" of a practical method. So the second challenge is, do you have a technique that you clearly understand, are capable of implementing and enjoy doing? In meditation, as in any other skill development, certain techniques work better for some people than for others. Indeed, you may find that you like different mindfulness techniques in different circumstances or that a mindfulness technique that works for you now changes over time. I will

provide clear instruction on a range of techniques, giving you ample opportunity to pick those that appeal to you.

3   How do I find the time? We are all truly busy, with many demands on our time. But the hidden assumption behind this challenge is that mindfulness can only be practised one way—seated in stillness. It then becomes just one more item on your already lengthy to-do list. Not so! Throughout this book, I will encourage you to practise mindfulness in a broad range of situations, whether sitting, in motion or in mindful moments during your day. Having a variety of meditation techniques means you can pick and choose different methods for different situations. Practising in different ways and at different times means you can quickly build a critical mass of skills so you can enjoy the rewards of mindfulness sooner. These rewards set up a positive feedback loop, a virtuous cycle that encourages you to keep practising and builds a sustainable habit.

4   How do I integrate mindfulness into my life? After learning basic techniques and tasting some rewards, most people ask, "How can I do more of this?" Later, I will guide you in developing your own Practice Map for Conscious Living, helping you integrate mindfulness practice into your life. More practice means greater skill. At first you are able to bring mindful awareness into simple tasks (a household chore); later you can bring heightened mindful awareness into the midst of challenging situations (a difficult conversation). As your skill levels become permanently elevated—and new neural pathways become solidly carved out—mindfulness will become not just one more item on your to-do list but integral to how you go about everything in your life.

5   How do I know if it's working? Here's where mindfulness has a unique challenge. For a habit to be successfully wired into your brain, the reinforcement for new behaviour needs to occur quickly and feel good. Think of the instant hit you get from great sex or delicious food, encouraging you to want more. Yet in mindfulness, the reinforcement of positive rewards may be subtle or take a while to occur. The rewards may be not the presence of a positive signal so much as the gradual absence of negative signals, for example, stresses that are diminished or reactivity that has been dialled down. It's like looking in the rear-view mirror of your car; you don't see much until you realize that you are no longer being followed by that huge, belching truck that's been tailing you for miles! If you don't get an instant feel-good reward, you may be inclined to think it's not working and so give up. I will address this challenge in three ways: by giving a variety of mindfulness methods and ways to practise, so that you can reach critical mass sooner, experience the positive rewards and build the positive feedback loop required for a sustainable habit; by regularly reviewing how your practice is going, so that you will be able to notice these subtle signals; by previewing now the range of positive impacts, so that you know where to look in your review process.

The Transformations

What would you look for to know whether mindfulness is working for you? Intuitively, you might assess by the experiences you have while you are meditating. You might think a calm, relaxed state means you are doing it right, while a fidgety body and busy mind means you are doing it wrong. I want to warn you right now: Don't go there! Yes, you could experience an immediate feeling of calm or heightened awareness. (I wasn't so lucky.) But these immediate experiences, whether positive or negative, are not a reliable indicator of long-term outcomes.

Every period of mindfulness practice is different. You could be having a good day. You sit down to do your usual practice and find your body is calm and your mind is alert. The next day is a rough day. You do the same practice and find your body agitated and your mind racing. This is not a reflection on you, whether you're doing the practice correctly or whether it's working. It's more like an accurate weather report from MoMo. The noted meditation teacher Ken McLeod says that practising meditation is like staying in a boat.[35] Imagine yourself in a one-person boat, like a kayak or small fishing boat. Some days, the water is smooth and your ride is effortless. Other days, the water is choppy and it's all you can do to stay upright. Mindfulness practice is like that. Your job is to stay in the boat, regardless of the weather. Over time, you learn how to navigate all conditions.

All mindfulness teachers—indeed all spiritual leaders—say the way to judge the efficacy of your practice is by looking to the long-term effects on your life. It takes time to build a skill, so it will take some time for the impact to show up in your life.

You will know you have changed when you behave, think or feel in a way that you previously could not have. Over the longer term (months to years), you can expect positive changes in one or more of the following areas: functioning more effectively in life, a general relief of suffering, a general increase in fulfillment, knowing yourself at a deeper level or exhibiting a greater sense of compassion or connection.

After establishing mindfulness practice, be alert to the developments that follow:

Are You Functioning More Effectively in Life?

Most people start mindfulness practice because they are stressed and want to be able to respond to the demands in their lives more effectively. When you are less stuck in your default patterns (our friend DAN again), you are more able to respond in ways that meet the situation of the moment, rather than reacting in predictable but ineffective ways. More effective functioning may include improved focus, greater calm, less emotional upset or personal reactivity and improved relationships. Or it can come about in improvements in specific behavioural challenges, such as losing weight, managing anger, sleeping better, procrastinating less or handling addictive behaviour. Or you may simply discern that your behaviours are not consistently in line with your deepest values and adjust your actions to be more in integrity with your aspirations. This ability to function more effectively builds the resilience muscle of an inner sense of control (resilience muscle #5).

Do You Notice a General Relief of Personal Suffering?

Mindful awareness skills can make you more effective in a range of situations, but they are not a magic wand. There may be some objective situations you cannot change or physical conditions that you must live with and learn to manage. When you cannot change the external circumstances of your life, you can learn how to accept the sensory experiences you are having. Through mindfulness, you learn that your perceived suffering is often magnified by your resistance to it. By not wanting to feel the way you do, you can make a difficult situation worse. The equation articulated by Shinzen Young is *suffering = pain × resistance*. You learn to diminish resistance in many ways: by breaking an experience down into its component parts of thinking, feeling and body sensations; by turning toward rather than turning away from a challenge; by developing self-compassion when you are in pain. When you lower your resistance, you can experience pain differently. (Remember Brian's story in Chapter 2, in which turning toward the experience of ice-pick headaches with non-resistance led to a dramatic relief of suffering.) You learn that while pain is unavoidable, suffering is optional.

A recent example of my own occurred when, halfway through a long-awaited family vacation, I slipped a disc in my back. The pain was so bad I couldn't get out of bed unaided. Years ago, I would have griped about this stupid accident ruining my vacation. Now I was able to direct all my attention toward the actual physical sensations, moving around tenderly as much as I could, adopting a slower, gentler gait. Despite several bad days, I still had a great vacation. I was able to experience the pain without running away from it. What would happen if you didn't have to push away the difficult experiences of life in order to cope?

Do You Notice a General Increase in Personal Fulfillment?

Sometimes you can drive toward big goals because you love the challenge or it's personally meaningful. But sometimes these drives are powered by a dull hole in our centre, a sense of not being in contact with the true vitality and pleasures of life. This can lead to addictive cravings for more and more that can never be truly sated. Because so much of our attention is caught up in DAN, we have little attention left over for MoMo—the actual moment-by-moment contact with pleasurable experiences. We think about other things or comment or worry about the pleasure experience itself. ("Is there enough? When will this end?")

It's as though ninety percent of our experience is stuck in our default attentional network and only ten percent is experiencing the actual moments of pleasure. We are not usually in full contact with the pleasures that life does offer. No wonder it's never enough! This lack of full contact is a kind of subtle interference, a resistance to taking in all of the momentary experiences. The inverse of resistance is equanimity, so: *fulfillment = pleasure x equanimity*. With resistance down, sensory pleasures become more fulfilling. With mindful awareness, you can learn to make full contact with the everyday pleasures of life, experiencing them fully, whether the taste of chocolate, the warmth of friendship, the beauty of nature or the satisfaction of a job well done. What would happen to your life if you could effortlessly touch small points of pleasure daily?

Do You Know Yourself at a Deeper Level?

If you are a competent, functioning adult, you likely have a good handle on your personality. You can describe yourself to others, list strengths at a job interview. This is a normal, surface level of self-awareness. When you engage in mindfulness meditation, you have the opportunity to see yourself at a deeper level. You may see for the first time the thoughts you are actually thinking, the emotions you are really feeling. They may not be what you "ought" to think or feel. But now you know. You become aware of your blind spots, your triggers, your assumptions, your true energy levels. You come to know what drives you at a deeper psychological level. This seeing is freeing. You can now respond from a deeper level, not tripping yourself up by repetitive patterns. The deepest level of self-awareness may come from contacting the source that is common to all humanity or all life.

Are You Becoming More Caring and Connected?

There is a paradox here. How can it be that becoming more aware of yourself makes you more caring for others? Yet with mindfulness, to become more aware of yourself, you must also become more accepting. Accepting yourself means it's easier to accept others, to touch your common humanity. Mindfulness also includes practices for deliberately cultivating positive feelings and intentions for yourself and others.

Anchoring Your Motivation

Through stories of ordinary heroes, a look at the scientific evidence and some understanding of the muscles of resilience and potential transformations, you now have an idea of what mindfulness can lead to. What is important to you now? The first step in any personal change is developing a sense of where you'd like to go and why. As an Integral Master Coach™, I always start a coaching program by helping my clients develop a topic statement. This statement articulates both the future vision of what success could look like and the current dissatisfaction that is driving you. This topic statement—and the reflection that goes into creating it—anchors your motivation, providing a compass for future inspiration when you need it. A topic statement is a critical tool in the early stages of the learning curve, the awkward moments when you wonder, "Why am I doing this, anyway?"

There are two steps in creating your Mindfulness Topic Statement.

The first step is to review the following checklist. Check off all the statements that apply to you. (You may want to take a first pass, then on further reflection, highlight your top three to five reasons.)

☐ I'd like to be more calm and focused under pressure.

☐ I'd like to improve my ability to persist through setbacks.

☐ I want to handle difficult feelings better, without letting emotions unduly distort my behaviour.

☐ I'd like to improve my general mood and sense of well-being.

☐ I'd like to fully experience a greater range and depth of pleasant emotions, for example, friendliness, humour, forgiveness, compassion, love, joy, peace . . .

☐ I'd like to improve my ability to respond to and manage daily stressors in my life.

☐ I'd like to feel a bit more in control of how I respond to situations as they arise.

☐ I'd like to reduce the suffering associated with physical health issues, whether sporadic or chronic.

☐ For painful situations I cannot change, I'd like to be able to experience them with less personal suffering.

☐ For pleasant situations that come my way, I'd like to be able to experience them with more personal fulfillment.

☐ I'm looking for a greater sense of personal meaning in my life.

☐ I want to understand the thoughts and feelings that drive me and the ones that trip me up.

☐ I want to understand the deeper levels of consciousness, from surface to source.

☐ I'm looking for deeper connections with people.

☐ I want some of the positive changes I've seen in others who have practised mindfulness.

☐ I'd like to handle stressful relationships in better ways.

☐ I'd like to improve my communications and relationships with others.

☐ I'm looking for greater personal wellness and healthy living.

☐ I want to be in contact with my body more often, or even for the first time.

☐ I'd like my actions to be more effective and productive.

☐ I want to more effectively live out the values and ethics I aspire to.

☐ I want help in addressing specific behavioural challenges or goals, for example, insomnia, healthy eating, long-standing habits or relational patterns.

☐ Mindfulness seems to provide a coherent map of how the mind works and I want to explore that further.

☐ I'm satisfied with the verifiable evidence for mindfulness and want to produce those results for myself.

The second step is to take a few moments to reflect on your answers in the checklist above. Are there any patterns that emerge? Anything that strikes you as most relevant or urgent? Make a few notes to yourself if you wish.

Now gather the checklist and your notes and develop them into the two statements that constitute your Mindfulness Topic Statement. The first statement represents your vision for mindfulness, what you would like this to enable for your future. The second statement represents the discomfort that you are experiencing now, the dissatisfaction that is driving you to change. Write these down here, in your own words.

Your Mindfulness Topic Statement

[Future Vision] I am interested in practising mindfulness because I would like to be more able to

_____

_____

_____

_____

_____

[Present Discomfort] This is important to me now because

_____

_____

_____

_____

_____

Practice: Deep Listening

If you wish to start practising now, here is a simple mindfulness practice that asks you to go deeply into the activity of listening. It is easiest to practise this in an environment where there are some sounds, although they don't necessarily need to be pleasant ones. First, let's review the basic instructions, then you can add on any variations you like.

BASIC INSTRUCTIONS FOR MINDFULNESS PRACTICE

1 Bring your body to an erect, dignified posture by sitting up straight—as though you were being pulled upward from the top of your head by a string—and then, from there, settle down into a relaxed position. Close your eyes fully or halfway, and place your hands lightly on your lap.

2 Bring your attention to the area inside your head, in between your ears. (This corresponds roughly to the auditory regions of the brain.) From here, focus your attention on whatever you can hear in your external environment.

3 If you notice that your attention wanders away from a focus on what you are hearing (to your thinking or to other physical sensations) gently bring it back to the activity of listening.

4 Repeat, repeat, repeat!

5 At the end of your session, do a quick review. Did you notice anything different? You may wish to jot down your experiences in a journal, to begin to record your experiences over time.

There are riffs and variations you can add to this simple mindfulness practice:

- Add further concentration by trying to detect your internal mental chatter: the voice in your head of inner running commentary.

- Add further clarity by getting curious about the range of different types of sounds you are hearing. Can you detect quiet as well as loud sounds? Nearby and faraway sounds?

- Add equanimity by attempting an even-handed acceptance of whatever you are hearing—pleasant or unpleasant sounds— and an intention of calm persistence if you lose focus on the activity of listening.

- Add a fun variation to this deep-listening practice with your favourite music. See if it enhances your experience. Can you detect the different instruments? Or the harmony among the vocalists?

What if you could practise deep listening in real time with a frustrated child or angry client? Deep listening is one application of the Unified Mindfulness System. Let me introduce you to the full system now.

[6]

The Unified Mindfulness System

U NIFIED MINDFULNESS is an integrated system that provides rigour and flexibility, consistency and variety. The rigour comes from a precise use of language, in both definitions and practice instructions. The flexibility comes from how you can adapt those practices every day. The consistency comes from a common framework for the many aspects of sensory experience and a core set of mindfulness skills. The variety comes from a range of meditation practices, each of which develops the same key skills.

It may take a little effort to understand the system, but once you do, you can adapt it to your own needs. By offering a variety of methods and different ways to practise, it allows you to avoid some of the pitfalls of mindfulness practice and to quickly develop a sustainable practice that is flexible enough to be tailored to your life and robust enough to help with your personal challenges. You may start wherever you like and proceed in any sequence, knowing that you are always developing the same fundamental skills. You can scale up or scale down the intensity of your training depending on what interests you or the opportunities, challenges or constraints you are facing. The methods in the rest of this book are an introduction to the Unified Mindfulness framework.

The Unified Mindfulness System offers the following:

- Three fundamental attentional skills (see below)

- Three types of practice, providing a framework for grouping similar mindfulness practices (see below)

- A variety of mindfulness practices, grouped under these three types, each of which develops the attentional skills (see Chapters 7 to 9)

- Ways to organize and integrate your practice for effectiveness and impact (see Chapters 10 and 11)

Three Attentional Skills

Mindfulness skills are a way to process your sensory experience. Any mindful awareness practice will be based on choices about where and how you direct your attention:

- Where you choose to direct your attention can be a very broad or very narrow range of focus. You can include anything happening inside you or around you; your inner world of thoughts, feelings and body sensations and the exterior world around you of physical sights and sounds. Since "anything happening inside or around you" is a very broad range, each of the techniques offered is based on different ways of dividing up this broad spectrum.

- How you choose to direct your attention is by developing three fundamental attentional skills: concentration, sensory clarity and equanimity. While I will go into these in more detail, for now
  - Concentration is the ability to focus on what you deem relevant at any given time.
  - Sensory clarity is the ability to detect and untangle the strands of your sensory experience.
  - Equanimity is the ability to allow sensory experience to come and go without push and pull.

So in the Unified Mindfulness framework: Mindful awareness is a certain way to pay attention to what is happening within you and around you, based on the working together of three attentional skills: concentration, sensory clarity and equanimity.

These attentional skills are natural, not something unique to meditation, but for most of us they are relatively underdeveloped. But we have all occasionally experienced high states of concentration, clarity or equanimity and have found these to be positive, productive states. (I'll illustrate this in the next few pages.) When you practise mindfulness, you grow the base level of these natural skills from a rudimentary level to a level of permanent elevation, sustaining you throughout your life. Things that used to require great effort or were available to you only in exceptional circumstances now become available effortlessly, regularly.

While each skill is distinct from the others, when all work together they reinforce one another. You learn how to let go, which sounds simple but—as we all know—isn't. Letting go requires a paradoxical combination of an effort of will (which comes from concentration and selective attention) and the surrender of will (which comes from equanimity, allowing sensory experiences to come and go as they will). Letting go of the past is an essential step in the process of resilience, learning and personal change.

Unified Mindfulness training is like comprehensive physical training. A complete exercise program includes workouts in cardio, strength and flexibility, providing a solid foundation for physical health. A complete mindfulness program will include training in concentration, sensory clarity and equanimity, providing a solid foundation for mental and emotional health.

Concentration

What comes to mind when you think of someone concentrating? Perhaps it's a tennis player focusing intently on her opponent, oblivious to any background noise. Or a business professional, shoulders hunched, staring at his screen, working furiously toward a looming deadline. Or a musician tuning in to his body as he plays his instrument and to the sounds and energy from his fellow musicians. We often think of concentration as being narrowly focused, unbroken over a long time, during which we tense up to suppress everything we're not concentrating on. No wonder it doesn't sound appealing!

In Unified Mindfulness, concentration is not about controlling the content of what you experience or suppressing anything in that experience. It is the skill of selective attention, consciously choosing where you direct your attention. Normally we associate concentration with focus and its inevitable by-product of tightening and tension. We think we can be either focused or relaxed, but not both. States of high concentration based on selective attention are characterized by focus *and* calm, relaxation and alertness.

Concentration is the ability to focus on what you consider to be relevant at any given time.

Have you ever experienced a situation in which you spontaneously fell into a state of high focus? Things seemed to slow down; you were calm, attuned and alert. You may have been aware of both your immediate challenge and the broader situation around you. You performed at your best: maybe your best ever. High-performing athletes and runners report this experience, calling it "being in the zone."

Looking back, I recall one time that I now recognize as falling into a state of high concentration—in this case, caused by worry and determination! I had promised our young girls a chance to visit their old home and friends a few weeks after we relocated. The day before we were to leave, I heard that truckers had threatened job action and highway closures. I briefly considered postponing our trip but couldn't bring myself to disappoint them. "We'll just leave bright and early, before the trucks block the road," I thought. I'm usually slightly tense and bossy when driving. On that day, without intention I dropped into a state of calm and focus, moving purposefully but not frantically. My driving was both crisp and flowing. The girls noticed the difference. "Gee, Mom, you're so relaxed!" We arrived safely at our destination well ahead of the road closures that never actually happened.

In Unified Mindfulness practice, you have several ways to develop concentration power.

First, you select something that, for that moment, you choose to pay attention to. We will call this "keeping an object in the foreground of your attention." It could be narrow, like the sensation of breathing in your diaphragm; or it could be broad, like the sound of birds and rustling leaves on a summer's day. It could be something pleasant, like your favourite music; or something unpleasant but unavoidable, like physical pain or emotional distress. You can choose to maintain your focus on this object of attention for several minutes or for much longer, up to several hours.

Second, you don't try to make everything you are *not* paying attention to go away. It won't; so don't even think about it! To the best of your ability, keep your focus on what you deem relevant in the foreground of your attention and let everything else play itself out in the background.

Third, when you notice that your attention has wandered off its selected focus, just calmly bring it back. Notice I said "when" not "if." When you are first practising, your concentration muscle is still wobbly and unstable. This is why you are training it in the first place, so please be patient yet persistent with yourself. You don't beat up a small puppy for doing what it can't help; you just guide it toward appropriate behaviours. Do yourself the same favour!

When your attention and energy are gathered in this way, you may sense a feeling of calm, settling in or internal steadiness. Your rate of breathing may slow down. Adults with regular lung capacity breathe somewhere in the range of fifteen to eighteen breaths per minutes. In states of high concentration, this may slow down to four to eight breaths per minute. Measure it for yourself by noting your respiration rate before and after a period of seated meditation practice.

Try this simple exercise in concentration.

Gaze at this picture. There are actually two images hidden in the picture. Which image do you see first, the horn player or the woman's face? (Hint: The woman's left eye is also the horn player's chin.) Now focus your attention on the image that you did *not* notice first. In other words, if you first noticed the horn player, place your attention on the woman's face. If you find the horn player jumping back at you, just refocus your attention on the face. Repeat this process as much as you need to over a period of several minutes.

What did you find by the end of this concentration exercise? Were you able to detect the secondary image more quickly? Did the secondary image become more stable for you? What would you say about your state of relaxation versus alertness? Notice that neither the foreground nor the background disappeared, but you were selectively directing your attention.

Sensory Clarity

If you're functioning well in life, you probably assume that you notice what's going on quite clearly. Yet how many times have you tripped up because you missed a critical detail? Or witnessed miscommunication because someone didn't hear the key words or see subtle body language? Sensory clarity is both an attitude of curiosity and the skill of bringing precision to your present-moment experiences. It can help us move beyond what we expect to perceive to notice what is actually there.

The well-researched concept of confirmation bias tells us that we see what we expect to see. In order to function, our brains need to filter out extraneous data. Over time, they develop patterns of filtering based on past experience. These patterns shape our expectations for the future. We literally do not perceive data that fall outside of these expectations. One recent study asked a group of radiologists to examine a series of chest X-rays just as they would if looking for lung cancer. Unbeknownst to the radiologists, though, the researchers had inserted into the X-rays a picture of something no professional would ever expect to see: a gorilla. The picture of the gorilla wasn't tiny; it was about forty-five times the size of the average cancerous lung nodule. How many radiologists missed the gorilla? Some eighty-three percent—even though eye tracking showed that most of them had looked right at it.[36]

Sensory clarity is the ability to keep track of what you are experiencing in the moment, detecting and untangling the strands of your sensory experience.

Our usual state of sensory clarity is akin to the quality of old movies or analogue television: adequate but fuzzy. High levels of sensory clarity, on the other hand, are like having high-definition TV, with more precision in the underlying streaming.

We perceive with more vividness and become more aware of subtle detail. Or, put another way, it's like shining a flashlight on the surface of a lake. At first, you're aware only of an opaque murkiness. With time and a stronger beam of light, you see that the murkiness is composed of tiny algae; you can see through it to the fish and plants below.

Perhaps you have had a peak experience of heightened sensory clarity, when your senses suddenly became brighter and clearer. It could have been inspired by the intensity of a beautiful sunset, some deeply moving music or the silken touch of a lover or baby. Some people, like me, enjoy travel or adventure because new sights and sounds invite us to perceive small details we usually wouldn't notice. Developing the muscle of sensory clarity means that more of these vivid details and rich distinctions become available to you every day.

In Unified Mindfulness, you develop sensory clarity by bringing an attitude of curiosity to whatever it is you are experiencing. You develop the skill to discern the separate strands of experience and detect what is occurring at a deeper level.

For example, let's say you're experiencing a distressing emotion like fear, sadness or shame. You use your concentration power to stay with the emotion rather than avoid it. You use sensory clarity to check it out in detail. What part of this experience is inner talk in your head? What part is subtle internal mental images? What part is emotional sensations in your body? Exactly where in your body do these sensations reside? How strong would you rate the intensity of these sensations? Are they stable or do they morph and change over time? Then you use equanimity to allow this experience to come and go as it will.

I find that sensory clarity is the secret sauce of mindful awareness and often overlooked in favour of concentration and equanimity. Clarity in our sensory experience allows us to untangle experiences that would otherwise be overwhelming, such as distressing emotions or physical pain. Like any large puzzle or problem, we may find the whole unmanageable, but when we chunk things down into smaller components, we can handle each one with relative ease.

With skill and practice, sensory clarity becomes highly developed and brings a taste of vividness and aliveness to life. Things don't look objectively different, but you are more aware of them at a granular level. They seem more alive with presence. It is the very opposite of a hazy, dreamy state, which is a dissociation from experience. This vividness can give rise to insights that show you more about experience. For example, by noticing small details in body language, you realize your colleague is dead tired today, so you don't take her apparently snide remark personally.

Try this simple exercise in sensory clarity. Look for several minutes at something that you see every day but don't usually pay much attention to. This could be trees in the distance, a streetscape or a picture hanging on the wall. Use your concentration power to keep gazing at it. Bring an attitude of light curiosity: What else do you notice? Zoom in to different details or shift your gaze around to different locations (left, right, centre, periphery, colour, shape). If you're bored, just stay with that and keep gazing. After a few minutes, do a review. Did you notice anything new? What did the quality of your attention feel like?

Equanimity

Equanimity might not be what you think it is. It is not the "whatever" attitude of someone who's indifferent to outcomes or unwilling to take a stand on important issues. It is not someone's passive behaviour or expressions. It is not the suppression of thoughts or feelings deemed unacceptable. We rightly shy away from these interpretations of equanimity because they are signs of unhealthy dissociation or denial. Equanimity is an attitude of openness and the skill of allowing experience to be as it is. Equanimity is like radical permission to feel, regardless of whether you like what you're feeling or not.

Equanimity is the ability to allow sensory experience to come and go without pushing it away or holding on to it.

The key to understanding equanimity is that it is relevant to your subjective sensory experience, not your objective behaviour in the world. It is a way of not interfering with or resisting the experience you are having—your being—which paradoxically allows you to be freer in your doing. Equanimity is a third way that does not attempt to cope with experience by suppressing, denying or resisting it, nor by identifying or fixating on it. Equanimity can show up in various flavours of openness throughout your entire being. In the mind, it is spacious curiosity. In the body, it is a sense of relaxation. And in the will or heart, it is a sense of even-handed kindness, acceptance of your experiences just as they are.

I experienced spontaneously dropping into equanimity on a canoe trip with my husband. It was on the last of three sunny, bug-free autumn days, when we noticed thunderclouds in the distance. We quickly packed up. I was worried that our rented aluminum canoe would become a magnet for lightning. After a few hours we heard the rumbling of thunder. We were on a river stretch between cliffs and swamp with no spots for landing, so I gave my paddling all I had. Then I noticed a tensing of fear in my shoulders and blaming, angry thoughts like, "How could he get us into this mess?" Somehow, when I became mindful of the anger, it just seemed silly. It dropped away. With this, my best-ever stroke suddenly had way more power in it. Who knew that so much energy was trapped in emotions?

This story illustrates that equanimity is the inverse of resistance. It is a way to dissolve our tendency to suppress, tighten or fixate. Resistance, or non-equanimity, acts to congeal, amplify or block our sensory experiences. By learning the skill of equanimity, we diminish the resistance that leads to unnecessary suffering or limits the potential for fulfillment, as we saw earlier in our two magic equations.

Suffering = pain × resistance

Fulfillment = pleasure × equanimity

When you bring equanimity to a situation, reducing resistance, your experiences and energy can flow more readily, as did the energy trapped in my feeling of irritation while paddling.

In Unified Mindfulness, you have several ways to develop the skill of equanimity. You can intentionally create equanimity in the body by attempting to maintain a relaxed state throughout your whole body. You can intentionally create equanimity in the mind by attempting to suspend negative judgments and replace them with an attitude of acceptance and gentle matter-of-factness. Importantly, you can notice when equanimity spontaneously just happens. The more you are alert to these opportunities, the more frequently they will occur and the longer they will last.

With practice and the development of some skill in concentration and sensory clarity, you can learn to detect a distinct "taste" of equanimity. It's a bit more subtle than the ready calm that comes from concentration. It can feel like a sense of openness or relaxation. Or it can feel a bit like the gritty abrasive I used to use on my teenaged skin—coarse but somehow also cleansing.

Try this simple exercise in equanimity. The next time you are feeling tense or stressed, sit down for five minutes and place your attention over your whole body. Notice where the tension is; this could be your shoulders, jaw, forehead, chest, stomach. Every time you become aware of tensing, intentionally relax to whatever degree you can. A moment later, you may notice the tension again in the same area or another. Again, just relax those areas to the best of your ability. If you cannot relax them, simply observe them, adopting as best you can an attitude of accepting the sensations just as they are, without wishing they would go away. After the exercise, what do you notice? If the tension is the same but you are less bothered by it, then you have experienced some equanimity.

Three Types of Practice

Various meditation practices that are now taught in different programs were originally developed and practised in isolation from one another. Each cultural tradition had its special favourites. In the twenty-first century we can now bring these practices together. So we need a way to organize them. I have chosen to integrate the practices into three broad types that correlate with our contemporary psychological knowledge of the process of personal development according to Scharmer's U curve that we saw in Chapter 4. The three types of practice that correlate to the U curve are Appreciate Self and World, Transcend Self and World and Nurture Positive in Self and World. Here is an overview of the three types and the meditation practices included in each.

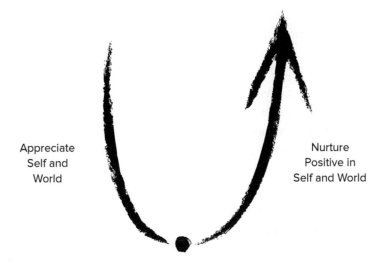

Appreciate Self and World   Nurture Positive in Self and World

Transcend Self and World

Appreciate Self and World includes mindfulness practices aimed at experiencing the senses with radical freedom and fullness. We suspend our automatic ways of thinking, feeling and behaving—DAN—by paying greater attention to moment-by-moment events—MoMo. We appreciate ourselves and the world just as we are. Paradoxically, by deeply observing and not trying to change anything, we do open up to change. We start to look *at* the senses, thoughts and feelings that we are used to looking *through*, thereby disidentifying from what had previously been unconscious patterns. With unconscious patterns now visible, we react automatically less often. With new data coming from MoMo, we are more able to respond in nuanced ways. It is as if our normal sense of self is like a tightly woven basket, with strands densely bound together. Mindful attention starts to loosen the weave of the basket, with more information being allowed to filter in. When we can move beyond the narrow constraints and instant reactions of DAN, we are free to respond in new and more adaptive ways.

Transcend Self and World are practices that enable us to contact something beyond the senses. Now that the basket weave of our being is looser, we can allow the new to flow into us, in between the mesh. We touch the unknown by directing our attention toward the edges of what we can detect with our ordinary senses and our conceptual mind. We open ourselves to the unknown, cultivating the ability to rest in uncertainty, to be in a transition space. We allow the sacred to touch us. We move from being the meditator to the one who is meditated.

Nurture Positive in Self and World are ways to refine your selfhood, to create a new version of DAN. Our default self is always changing, as we grow and mature in experience. You can see this as you look back on yourself five, ten or twenty years ago. "Nurture Positive" allows us to direct this growth with the values or aspirations meaningful to us. We do this by selectively attending to positive emotions, rational healthy thinking and positive behaviours. With the basket weave of our self now loose and open to the new, we can actively cultivate new qualities, direct our aspirations and change our personal narratives in new and healthy ways. This is the place for compassion practices, visualization and intention setting, cognitive reframing or prayer. It is where you go beyond your current way of being to develop a newer way of being that is both more compassionate and more effective in the world.

Sitting Practice: Time, Place and Posture

We will delve into the various mindfulness methods in the next chapter. In the meantime, now that you have anchored your motivation and learned a breath practice, you might want to try practising on a regular basis. Like any skill, meditation is learned by doing. Ultimately, you'll be able to implement one or more method at different times throughout your day, but for now let's start off simply. Practising while seated is by no means the only way to meditate. But it is the cornerstone of practice for many, as it is an easy way to be simultaneously relaxed and alert. Here are some guidelines for a regular sitting practice.

In order to foster an enduring habit, it helps to develop a routine—something that acts as a trigger for you, encouraging behaviours that ultimately become automatic. Like any new routine, it will feel awkward at first. If you're a person who detests routine, or whose life is anything but routine, then you can set yourself the creative challenge of building mindfulness practice into each day in innovative ways.

Time

Develop habits related to time:

- Aim for a minimum of ten minutes of seated practice, most days.

- Start small and scale up. When you feel comfortable with ten minutes, try going for twelve minutes, then fifteen minutes. Many people maintain a steady practice of twenty to thirty minutes each day. Others go for longer, up to forty or sixty minutes.

- Aim for consistency rather than length of time. Ten minutes most days is better than thirty minutes a few times a week. If you get disrupted, because of vacations, family, work demands and so on, try for even five minutes a day rather than nothing. You can retreat to the toilet stall for five minutes of practice if you have to! If you start and then end up doing nothing, don't beat yourself up. Just "get back on the wagon" and begin again.

- Try for a time in the day when things are quiet. For many, this means early in the morning, whether at home or at work, or before going to bed. For others, it could be sitting on the bus going to work. Most people have one time of day they prefer; others practise twice, at the beginning and end of their day, bookending their day with mindful awareness.

- Use a timer or app on your phone to set your time. Once you've set your timer, do your best to sit still until the end of your intended time. If you must move, do so with intention.

Place

Develop habits related to place or space:

- The most important thing is to have a place that is readily and consistently available to you. It need not be a special place, although some people like to use pictures, candles or special objects to remind them that this is their meditation spot. Quiet and undisturbed are also good but not always possible. If you don't have a door you can shut, you can always hang a "do not disturb" sign over yourself!

- The place itself could be a small room or, more likely, a corner of a room that you use every day. You can purchase special equipment, like meditation cushions or benches, or use whatever you have at hand. If you are using a chair, it helps to have one with a relatively straight back, like an office or kitchen chair. Some people use ergonomic chairs.

Posture

Is there an ideal body position for mindfulness meditation? Yes. You are seeking to develop a posture that expresses both relaxation and alertness: the very qualities of attention that mindfulness develops. The research of Dr. Amy Cuddy, a social psychologist at Harvard Business School, reveals that simply changing body positions can affect our body chemistry; changes in body can beget changes in mind.[37] This is especially relevant to mindfulness practice. We are used to being either alert and tense or relaxed and loose. You are developing a posture that embodies the best of both. If you are habitually alert, you may find that relaxation is difficult or that it's so unusual you nod off into sleepiness. If you are habitually relaxed, you may find it effortful to become alert. Think of it like riding a bike: too slow and you fall off; too fast and you can't stay on. Don't get too fussed about having the right posture right away; it may take a while to develop.

Despite stereotyped images, you don't need to sit in a contorted position on the floor. Cross-legged postures were started in Asia, where people's bodies have adapted to sitting or squatting rather than our Western habit of sitting on chairs. If you are reasonably comfortable you can sit on the floor, with legs crossed but ankles not on top of each other (i.e. "tailor style"). If you can manage it, you can sit in quarter, half or even full lotus. Large cushions or specially designed meditation cushions add comfort. If you sit on a chair, sit on the forward end of the chair, so that your back is held erect and unsupported. Here are the key points that will help you develop a posture that is both relaxed and alert:

- Spine straight and balanced
- Hips higher than knees

- Chest open with shoulders rolled back and down
- Head resting on neck with chin slightly inward, jaw slightly loose
- Eyes closed, open or half open
- Hands in a position that is both relaxed and alert

Alertness is facilitated by a straight back, your body weight balanced and evenly distributed over the pelvic bones, your head balanced evenly on your neck. A straight back is not in a straight line but more a gentle S-curve. You can overdo this natural curve by either arching or slouching. If you find yourself arching your back or neck, you are too tense, so adjust for greater ease and balance. If you find yourself slouching, you are too relaxed, so straighten up your spine. In time, you will develop the back muscles that can easily support an erect posture. Your doctor or chiropractor will thank you for this! Having your hips slightly higher than your knees also supports a straight back. You can help this with a cushion under your buttocks (on a chair or on the floor) or a cushion behind your back (on a chair).

Relaxation is encouraged in several ways. By dropping your jaw ever so slightly so that your teeth don't touch, you minimize jaw clenching and encourage a gentle release throughout the head and shoulder area. Eyes closed encourages concentration but can result in sleepiness. If you are too sleepy, either open your eyes or keep them in a half-open "far mountain gazing" position.

The hands should be in a position that is both relaxed and alert, for example, cupped on your lap, palms up, with the non-dominant hand resting on top of the dominant hand. (This encourages the dominant side of your body to relax.) If you need to adjust your posture during your practice time because you are uncomfortable, that's okay, but please do so with intention, not just because you're fidgeting.

What kind of practice can you do while you are seated? Any practice. You can focus on the breath or use any of the Unified Mindfulness System methods, which we will turn to now.

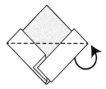

[7]

Practices to
Appreciate Self and World

PERHAPS YOU experienced a heightened state while practising the recent exercises for concentration, clarity and equanimity, or I've managed to convince you that mindfulness skills are worth having. How can you develop them in a consistent way? Over the next three chapters, I will present multiple mindfulness methods, grouped under the three themes of Appreciate Self and World, Transcend Self and World and Nurture Positive in Self and World. Taken together, these methods are a comprehensive approach based on tested meditation methods found around the world, but reworked so that they all share a common language. And they all adjust either *where* you direct your attention or *how* you direct your attention. However, you do not need to learn or practise all of them. You may choose a few that you like, or use different methods in different situations. So if variety appeals to you, dig in. If variety feels overwhelming, don't worry too much about choosing, since every method develops the same core skills of concentration, sensory clarity and equanimity.

We will start with methods in the "Appreciate" theme. Here we deeply observe ourselves and the world just as we are. We do not try to change anything, yet through acceptance of our experiences, we open ourselves up to change.

Feel-See-Hear

The Feel-See-Hear method is at the core of the Appreciate theme. When you practise Feel-See-Hear, you are exploring all your thinking, feeling and physical body sensations: all the sights and sounds of the world, all your interactions with others. That is a lot! Taken as a whole, all this sensory experience can be overwhelming; so overwhelming that you scurry back to the comforts of DAN. So we break down this large landscape through focus options that match our basic sensory processing. These we will call Feel-See-Hear. If it helps to remember, you can call this FSH (like fish, without the "I.")

We'll go into more detail soon, but first let's do a little ten-minute taste test of Feel-See-Hear.

FEEL-SEE-HEAR TASTE TEST

Sit in an upright yet relaxed posture that reflects both dignity and curiosity. Eyes closed for now. Start with somatic (body) experience as your focus range, directing your attention to any physical- or emotional-body experience for the first three to four minutes:

1   Bring your attention to your body, perhaps by starting in the central core of the body. Or attention could be focused anywhere: on the sensations of breathing, the physical sensations of contact on the chair or cushion, the gentle movements of stomach or muscles, the sense of physical relaxation or even the emotions coursing through your body. You can proceed with a systematic sweep, starting at the top of your head and moving down to your toes, or in a random fashion. The body is a vast world, so if you want to pick one smaller area, that's fine. (It could be the breath.)

2   Every few seconds (three to five) gently but intently focus on one aspect of body that you are experiencing now, and speak internally the label "Feel." This label helps to anchor you in what you are noticing. So if I were to listen inside your head, I would be hearing "Feel... Feel... Feel..." Use a gentle, matter-of-fact tone in your labelling. If your attention wanders away from body experience, for example, to external sounds or internal thoughts, gently bring it back.

3   Repeat over and over, and enjoy getting to know the universe of your body.

    Proceed to visual experience as your focus range, directing your attention to anything that you see internally with your eyes closed or externally with your eyes open for the next three to four minutes.

4   Bring your attention to visual space: the area in your head just behind your eyes. You will use this as home base from which to explore visual experience, both interior to the mind's eye and exterior to the world of light and sight. What do you see from there?

5 With your eyes closed, look at your internal visual screen (a.k.a. the mind's eye). You could be seeing visual images or a lightness, darkness or grey-scale blank. Get curious about what you're noticing.

6 Every few seconds (three to five), gently but intently focus on one particular aspect of your visual experience now, and speak internally the label "See." Repeat internally to yourself the label "See... See... See...," which helps anchor you on what you're noticing.

7 Now open your eyes halfway, so that you have the impression of light but not forms. What do you see from this relaxed, in-between space? Repeat the label "See... See... See..."

8 Now open your eyes completely, the way you would in daily life, so that you are seeing colour and form. Explore in the same way: What do you see from there? Repeat the label "See... See... See..."

Proceed to auditory experience as your focus range, directing your attention to anything that you hear outside or inside your head for the final three to four minutes.

9 Bring your attention to auditory space, the area in your head between your ears. You will use this as home base from which to explore auditory experience, both the interior sounds of the monologue inside your head (the default narratives of our friend DAN) and the exterior sounds of the world. What do you hear from here? You can have your eyes closed or open, as you prefer.

10 Every few seconds (three to five), gently but intently focus on one aspect of auditory experience now, and speak internally

the label "Hear." So if I were to listen inside your head, I would be hearing "Hear... Hear... Hear..." Use a gentle, matter-of-fact tone in your labelling. If your attention wanders away from auditory experience, gently bring it back.

11 Repeat, over and over, until your timer goes off.

Noting

Feel-See-Hear describes one parameter of mindfulness; exploring more deeply *where* you direct your attention. The other parameter is *how* you pay attention. You have already practised this just now, when you "gently but intently" focused on some aspect of experience and used a label to help you monitor your experience. This process is called noting. Since you are separating the strands of sensory experience into distinct streams, you have the luxury of diving deeply into how you are experiencing each one. If Feel-See-Hear helps you explore the vast world of moment-by-moment experience, noting helps you go beyond the superficial glance that is usually required of MoMo. With noting, you deeply experience all your senses.

You can compare noting to looking through a microscope. Your everyday attention is like looking at a speck of dirt, perhaps wondering if you should wash your hands. With noting attention, it is like your eyes (indeed all of your senses) are able to see at much greater magnification: noticing details, gradations and connections that weren't available to you before.

Noting develops mindful awareness by clearly acknowledging the existence of sensory experiences, then gently, intently focusing on them at a pace that works for you.

Noting consists of a rhythmic pulsing of deep acts of attention, paced in a way that works for you (for example, every three to five seconds). Each pulse has two parts:

1   An initial noticing or acknowledging of a particular sensory event
2   A short period of intently focusing on that experience

While you are noting, you can use a label. Labels are mental or spoken words that name the specific sensory experience you are focusing on at that moment. You can speak the label internally or, when appropriate, say it out loud. In the Feel-See-Hear method the labels are—surprise—"Feel," "See" and "Hear." With noting, you work on the three core skills:

- You develop concentration by maintaining a steady, rhythmic pacing, for example, every three to five seconds. If you notice that you've stopped labelling and noting, it's a clue you're lost somewhere.

- You develop sensory clarity by the intent focusing of step 2 above, by noticing subtle distinctions in your experience and by bringing an attitude of curiosity and exploration to your practice.

- You develop equanimity by using a gentle, matter-of-fact tone in your labelling and by cultivating an attitude of even-handed acceptance of whatever is occurring just now.

When you are noting, you are not trying to understand something or figure it out. That is called thinking! Instead you are observing and moving on: that is the sound of a dove; there goes a car; that is the laughter of someone down the hall.

Feel-See-Hear Practice

Let's go into a bit more detail on the Feel-See-Hear method, so that you can practise in confidence on your own. First I'll provide the steps in the process, then show you the general grid that offers an overview of these practices, then give a bit more detail on each method.

FEEL-SEE-HEAR PRACTICE STEPS

1 Decide what your focus range will be for at least the first few minutes. This could be somatic, visual or auditory space.

2 Direct your attention to this designated space. Think of your attention as something you can consciously direct, like a billiard ball. With practice, your aim will be both steady and relaxed.

3 Begin the rhythmic sequence of noting, using the label "Feel," "See" or "Hear" to help anchor you.

4 Repeat the process over and over within that focus range for your intended time, with a suggested minimum of three to five minutes.

5 When you're done, you can move on or continue in that space as you wish. You can decide in advance the sequence you will follow or intentionally shift your focus range, depending on what occurs during your practice time. Enjoy!

General Grid of Sensory Experience

This is a summary of the four methods that Feel-See-Hear comprises, where to place your attention, the label to use and the range of content you may experience. I'll go into more detail on each one shortly.

Name of Method	Place of Attention	Label	Range of Content
Just Feel	**Somatic space:** In, over or slightly outward from your whole body, including both the objective physical body and the subjective emotional body	"Feel"	Active or restful physical-body sensations, active or restful emotional-body sensations, body flow states
Just See	**Visual space:** In your head, in the space just behind your eyes looking outward to what you see externally (with eyes open) or inward to your internal mental screen (with eyes closed)	"See"	Physical sights, mental images, visual restful states, visual flow states
Just Hear	**Auditory space:** In your head, in the space further back between your ears, hearing whatever you hear externally (physical sounds or silence) or internally (internal mental talk)	"Hear"	Physical sounds, mental talk, auditory restful states, auditory flow states
Note Everything	Unrestricted focus range; all of the above	"Feel," "See" or "Hear"	You note whatever comes or calls
Optional label for any method		"Gone"	

A Short Note about "Gone"

You can also use the label "Gone" in any of these methods. "Gone" applies when all or part of an experience suddenly drops or disappears, *and* you happen to notice it. This could be the end of a sound, the end of an exhalation or the disappearance of an image on your TV. Noticing subtle "Gones" sharpens the skill of sensory clarity. Experiencing the "Gones" of our ever-changing, transient world contributes to the skill of equanimity. Use this label only if you wish and only if you happen to notice the disappearance of something. You will meet "Gone" again in the "Transcend Self and World" theme in Chapter 9.

Just Feel: Focus on Somatic Experience

With Just Feel, you are exploring any and all kinds of somatic experience, both of the objective physical body and the subjective emotional body.

Place your attention in somatic space, in and over your whole body, or even extending slightly outward from the body. You can start in the body core or in the body as a whole envelope. You can start at the top of the head and proceed systematically down to your toes (similar to a body-scan technique). Or you can start anywhere you like and proceed as you like.

The range of content that may be available to you in somatic space includes:

- Active physical-body sensations, for example, skin and sense of touch, breathing, taste, smell, interior organs such as stomach, bladder, heartbeat, muscles, spine

- Restful physical-body sensations, for example, physical relaxation, muscle release or the sensations of muscles that are not actively working

- Active emotional-body sensations, when you experience a body sensation that at the time you judge to be emotional in nature (this can change; a rapid heartbeat could be because of fear or a good run)

- Restful emotional-body sensations, such as the absence of strong emotional signals

- Body flow states, such as tingling, pulsing, vibrating, undulating and so on, in part or all of your body

Every few seconds, you direct your attention to some aspect of bodily experience. As you become aware of a sensation in the body, you note it. If you wish to use a label to support the noting, it is "Feel." This label can refer to a wide range of experiences: the sensations of your feet on the floor, the beating of your heart, the breath moving through your chest, tension in your jaw. So if I were listening inside your head, every few seconds I would hear "Feel... Feel... Feel...," although the same label might be referring to different experiences. Remember that you are using the label not to keep track of every single somatic experience but to keep yourself anchored in somatic space.

If you wish to use the label "Gone," it is quite easy to apply in Just Feel: to the end of a breath, body twitch, taste or touch or to the sudden diminishing of an ache or pain.

You develop concentration skill by selectively attending only to somatic experience. If your attention is drawn into anything you're thinking, seeing or hearing, gently redirect it back to body experience. You develop equanimity by letting other modalities be in the background and by having no preference for what kind of body experiences you are having, be they pleasant or unpleasant. (This is why some people at least occasionally sit for a longer period of time—to develop the skill of equanimity by dealing with aches and sleepiness.) You develop sensory clarity by detecting the shape, location, intensity and duration of the body's many sensations available to you, by learning to detect subtle restful states that are available or may be cultivated, by detecting and being massaged by energetic flow states within the body and by learning to detect subtle flavours of emotions within the body.

JUST FEEL PRACTICE

1 Direct your attention to your body, to sensations in, all over or slightly beyond your body. Include active body sensations, restful body sensations, emotional body sensations or flowing body sensations.

2 Begin the rhythmic sequence of noting within somatic space; each act of noting is an initial noticing of a body sensation, then a short period of intently focusing on it.

3 If you wish to use a label, it is "Feel."

4 If all or part of a body sensation suddenly drops or disappears, and you happen to notice it, you can choose to use the label "Gone."

5 Repeat the process, with a suggested minimum of three to five minutes.

Just See: Focus on Visual Experience

With Just See, you are exploring any and all kinds of visual experience, including both the external sights of the world and the inner images of the mind's eye. You can practise with your eyes open, halfway open or closed.

Place your attention in visual space, in the area inside your head just slightly behind your eyes (roughly corresponding to the visual processing components of the brain). With your eyes open, you can direct your attention outward to the physical sights all around you. With your eyes closed, you can direct your attention internally to what you see behind your eyelids when your eyes are closed. We will call this your internal mental screen. Colloquially we call it the mind's eye.

The range of content that may be available to you includes the following:

- When your eyes are open, any physical sights that you see, whether those objects are fixed or moving

- When your eyes are lightly open but relaxed, whatever you see with a soft, defocused gaze, such as shades of light and dark

- When your eyes are closed, any actively present images that you see on your internal mental screen

- When your eyes are closed, an absence of images on your internal mental screen—a restful state of lightness, darkness or grey-scale blank

- Visual flow states that, with eyes open, could be the movement of actual objects, or with eyes closed, could be the movement of internal images; or it could be any kind of pixelation, swirling or twinkling in your visual field

If you are labelling, it is "See." So if I were listening inside your head, every few seconds I would hear you labelling, "See... See... See..."

If you wish to use the label "Gone," you can do so with your eyes open (easier to detect) or with your eyes closed (harder to detect). With your eyes open, "Gone" could be applied to the disappearance of something (a bird flies out of your range of vision; the passing of people or objects as you are walking along). With your eyes closed, this could include the ending of an internal visual image.

You develop concentration by selectively attending to only visual experiences. Whenever you find your attention pulled into anything that you are hearing or feeling, just gently redirect your attention back to visual experience. You develop equanimity by not shutting out or suppressing other experiences. When you are doing Just See, you will almost certainly hear ambient sounds and feel some bodily sensations. This is fine. Just let them be in the background of your awareness, and place visual experience in the foreground. Even if these other experiences are quite strong or unpleasant, do not judge the experiences as bad or yourself as getting it all wrong. Attempt to note and greet all experiences equally, whether they are pleasant or unpleasant. You develop sensory clarity by learning to detect the varying flavours and intensity of visual experiences, ranging from small visual details and variations in the colour and form of physical sights to increasing familiarity with the content, shape and movement of visual images on your internal mental screen.

JUST SEE PRACTICE

1   Direct your attention to the visual sights that you see with your eyes open *or* to the internal mental images or grey-scale blank that you see on your inner mental screen when your eyes are closed.

2   Begin the rhythmic sequence of noting within visual space; each act of noting is an initial noticing of an external sight or internal image, then a short period of intently focusing on it.

3   If you wish to use a label, it is "See."

4   If all or part of a sight or visual image suddenly drops or disappears, and you happen to notice it, you can choose to use the label "Gone."

5   Repeat the process, with a suggested minimum of three to five minutes.

Just Hear: Focus on Auditory Experience

With Just Hear, you are exploring any and all kinds of auditory experience, including both the external sounds of the world and the internal sounds and voices in your head. These inner monologues and commentaries are the auditory component of your thinking process. Taken together, internal images on the mental screen and internal mental talk constitute your thinking.

Place your attention in auditory space, which is the area roughly in the centre of your head, between your ears. It's a little farther back in the head than the home base for visual space. From here, direct your attention externally to the sounds of the world around you or internally to the sounds of your internal thinking.

The range of content that may be available to you includes the following:

• Active external sounds that you hear when your attention is directed outward to the sounds of the world

- Restful states that you detect when your attention is directed outward, such as silence and the absence of sound

- Active internal sounds that you hear when your attention is directed inward to the sounds of your inner mental talk or, for example, a song stuck in your head

- Restful states that you detect when your attention is directed inward, such as the mental quiet that is the absence of inner talk

- Auditory flow states, such as a background hum in the external silence or a sense of subtle stirring underneath mental talk

If you are labelling, it is "Hear." So if I were listening inside your head, every few seconds I would hear you labelling "Hear... Hear... Hear..."

If you wish to use the label "Gone," this could include the end or sudden diminishing of any external sounds or any internal mental chatter.

You develop concentration skill by selectively attending only to auditory experiences. Whenever you find your attention is pulled into anything you are feeling or seeing, redirect your attention to auditory space. You develop equanimity by greeting both pleasant and unpleasant sounds in the same even-handed way—like welcoming both noisy and quiet children equally—and by letting other visual or somatic experiences be in the background. You develop sensory clarity by detecting variations in tone and movement of what you are hearing externally and by discerning content and movement of your internal mental talk.

JUST HEAR PRACTICE

1   Direct your attention to the auditory sounds that you hear, either the sounds of the external world or the inner sounds inside your head.

2   Begin the rhythmic sequence of noting within auditory space; each act of noting is an initial noticing of an external or internal sound, then a short period of intently focusing on it.

3   If you wish to use a label, it is "Hear."

4   If all or part of an auditory external sound or inner talk suddenly drops or disappears, and you happen to notice it, you can choose to use the label "Gone."

5   Repeat the process, with a suggested minimum of three to five minutes.

Note Everything: Focus on Everything

With Note Everything, you do not restrict your focus range to any one modality. This can be interesting if you like variety or if you find restricting your range to be too taxing. It is not suitable if you find it too complex, if there is too much going on or if you find that your meditation experience is indistinguishable from your usual wandering mind.

With the Feel-See-Hear focus range, your contact stance is intentional; you are actively directing your attention to a particular space. With Note Everything, your contact stance is responsive. You do not consciously direct your attention to any one space but "lie back" and note whatever sensory experience arises or calls to your attention.

When you are noting in Note Everything, it's easiest to use just one label at a time. So if I were listening inside your head, I could be hearing, "Feel... Feel... See... Hear... Hear... See... See... Feel... Feel..." However, if you feel up to it, you can note two things at a time, for example, "Feel and See," "Feel and Hear," "See and Hear," "See and Feel," "Hear and See," "Hear and Feel."

NOTE EVERYTHING PRACTICE IN FEEL-SEE-HEAR

1   Let your attention go to whatever sensory experience arises or calls to you. This could be any aspect of somatic, visual or auditory space.

2   Begin the rhythmic sequence of noting; each act of noting is an initial noticing of a sensory experience, then a short period of intently focusing on it.

3   If you wish to use labels, they are "Feel," "See" or "Hear."

4   If all or part of a sensory experience suddenly drops or disappears, and you happen to notice it, you can choose to use the label "Gone."

5   Repeat the process, with a suggested minimum of three to five minutes.

Example of a Feel-See-Hear Practice Session

This is an illustration of how an actual practice session might be experienced:

You like to practise on a chair and have found a comfortable straight-backed chair. Since you know you tend to slouch and you're tired after a long day, you've put a cushion under your buttocks to keep your back straight by raising your hips higher than your knees. You've set the timer on your phone for twelve minutes. Since you're not feeling particularly energetic, you decide to practise Feel-See-Hear in sequence, then toward the end decide if you're up for Note Everything. You close your eyes to encourage relaxation.

You start by placing your attention in the core of your body and adjusting your body. Since you're feeling tense, you deliberately raise and then lower your shoulders and drop your jaw slightly so your teeth are not touching. Right away you notice some release of tension. "Feel ... Feel ..." Then you direct your attention from the top of the head all the way down to your toes. For the first few passes you do this at an even pace. But then you notice some aches and tensions, so you linger a bit longer at those spots. "Feel ... Feel ..." After a while, you notice that you're thinking about a recent situation at work, which might just be why you're tense. Ooops—away from thinking. Redirect attention back to the body.

Now that you're a little more relaxed and concentrated, you decide to move on to "See." You redirect your attention up into the head, just behind your eyes, keeping your eyes closed. You're a strong visual thinker and internal mental images come readily to you. You notice various images and after a bit, you notice one image having to do with the situation at work. You decide to turn directly toward this image and see if you can maintain some kind of equanimity with this unpleasant memory. To help induce equanimity, you speak the label "See" out loud, deliberately using a calm voice. (Even though you don't feel so even-handed just now.) You keep this up for a minute or so, then notice that you've forgotten the labelling and are "lost in thought."

Since your attention has gone to thinking, you decide this is a good time to move over to auditory space, and shift over to "Hear." For a few minutes, all you can detect is the inner dialogue of what you wished you'd said at work. But rather than getting swept up in it, you are noting it as mental chatter. "Hear... Hear..." However, this monologue in your head seems to start and stop. When you happen to notice a sudden dropping away, you note, "Gone..." You decide to stay in auditory space for the last few minutes, but direct attention away from your inner mental talk and toward external sounds—giving yourself a break! You're near a busy street and there are all kinds of sounds. "Hear... Hear..." Cars, sirens, voices, sometimes a few birds. Sometimes a gap in the sounds, with a hint of silence breaking through. "Hear... Hear..." Nothing is particularly amiss, so you just enjoy the sounds of city life.

It's been a busy mindfulness workout, so you decide to end your practice session with Just Hear. After your timer goes, you open your eyes, stretch a bit and do a quick review of your session. You're actually feeling a bit more relaxed and the situation at work isn't irritating you quite as much. On to the rest of your day.

[8]

Practices to Appreciate
Patterns in Self and World

I N CHAPTER 7, you learned about Feel-See-Hear as a way
to explore the richness of sensory experience beyond the
automatic patterns of DAN. You used the noting technique as
a way to penetrate deeply into whatever sensory experience you
were immersed in. Feel-See-Hear gives you a simple way to break
down overall sensory experience—which can be overwhelming—
into manageable bits, based on your natural sensory processing.

Here I want to offer you another way to break down overall
sensory experience, which I will call the Feel-See-Hear variation
methods. While Feel-See-Hear aligns to our natural senses, the
variation methods align with how we think of ourselves; me in
here, you and the world out there. So our mindfulness practice
can include distinctions between inner and outer experience.

The general Feel-See-Hear method also includes subtler
experiences, such as restful states and flowing states. However,

we don't usually notice them. For most people, attention goes first to obvious active experiences, such as physical sensations or external sights and sounds. Once you point out subtler experiences, such as physical rest, emotional-body sensations or exterior silence, they are much easier to detect. It's like trying to find a bird in a tree; once you know the colour and where to look, it jumps out at you. The four variation methods help us appreciate patterns in outer and inner, restful and flowing experiences.

"Subtle is significant," says Shinzen Young. We are often affected in ways we don't even know by subtle phenomena. Physical tension, fatigue, emotional strain, the inner monologue of what we're *really* thinking: all these affect us. If we're not aware of them—and mostly we're not— they can drive our behaviour. We find ourselves saying, "I couldn't help it." Or, "Where did that come from?" When you become aware of subtle phenomena, they can begin to inform your conscious choices rather than distort your unconscious behaviour. Becoming aware of your deeper patterns, you are able to change them or work with them more effectively.

Each of the four variation methods also has its unique benefits. Focusing Out on the external world helps you anchor in the richness of the world. Focusing In on the inner world helps you know yourself at the deepest level and untangle emotional knots. Focus on Rest provides ready access to deliciously calm states. Focus on Flow helps you come in contact with the ever-changing nature of our world—and of yourself.

The four variation methods also provide options for practice, so you can integrate mindfulness seamlessly into your day. Some techniques, such as Focus Out, can be readily applied when you're on the go. Some techniques, such as Focus In, are more readily applied when you're sitting in stillness.

Detailed Grid of Sensory Experience

In Chapter 7, I outlined a General Grid of Sensory Experience based on the senses of feeling, seeing and hearing. Now I'd like to extend this further by taking the range of content column and breaking it down into specific categories of outer, inner, restful and flowing content. All this does is add extra columns to the existing grid. With the General Grid of Sensory Experience, you work with the rows and the methods Just Feel, Just See, Just Hear. With the Detailed Grid of Sensory Experience, you work with the columns, discerning the particulars of yourself and the world. These become the methods of Focus Out, Focus In, Focus on Rest and Focus on Flow.

	Focus Out ↓	Focus In ↓	Focus on Rest ↓	Focus on Flow ↓
	On external world and our physical, objective body	On internal world and our subjective emotions	On restful states in both external and internal worlds	On flowing states in both external and internal worlds
"Feel"	Active physical-body sensations	Active emotional-body sensations	Physical rest: physical relaxation or emotional peacefulness	Flowing sensations in physical or emotional body
	"Feel Out"	"Feel In"	"Feel Rest"	"Feel Flow"
"See"	Active sights in the external world	Active internal visual images	Visual rest: defocused gaze externally or blank mental screen internally	Flowing sensations in external or internal visual space
	"See Out"	"See In"	"See Rest"	"See Flow"
"Hear"	Active sounds in the external world	Active internal mental talk	Auditory rest: exterior silence or interior mental quiet	Flowing sensations in external or internal auditory space
	"Hear Out"	"Hear In"	"Hear Rest"	"Hear Flow"

With Focus Out, you explore the outer world of sights and sounds around you, as well as your physical body.

With Focus In, you explore your inner subjective sense of self, the emotions in the feeling body and the inner visual images and mental talk that constitute your thinking process.

With Focus on Rest, you create or focus on naturally occurring restful states in the body or in visual or auditory spaces, internal or external.

With Focus on Flow, you focus on any kind of flowing, vibrating or bubbly types of sensations in any external, internal or restful states.

You work with the Detailed Grid using the same noting technique as before, directing your attention in rhythmic pulses, paced every few seconds. But now you are discerning very specifically where you are directing your attention. This is reflected in the use of labels, which are now two-part, for example, "Feel Out," "See Out," "Hear Out," "Feel In," "See In," "Hear In" and so on.

Focus Out

Doesn't it sound great when yoga instructors or seductive advertisements exhort you to "be here now"? How do you do that without going on vacation or to a spa? With Focus Out, you direct your momentary attention (MoMo) to external sights, sounds and physical (i.e. non-emotional) body sensations. All these momentary sensations of nature happen only in the now. By anchoring your attention out in the momentary sensations of nature and your natural body, you do live in the now, while deeply attuning yourself to the wonders of the world.

Focusing Out on the momentary sensations of the objective world by Feeling Out, Seeing Out and Hearing Out has several advantages. When you are coping with stress, worried or over-thinking, you can take a break by redirecting your attention away from unproductive or self-defeating habits of DAN toward the now of the senses. When you are engaged in enjoyable activities (or perhaps anticipating their imminent end), you can derive even more fulfillment by directing your momentary attention to fully savouring the experience. (Think workouts, sex or a cool beer on a hot day.) With Focus Out, you explore each or all of your physical-body sensations, and the external sights and sounds of the world. Let's review how to practise with each of the individual subcomponents and then collectively.

Feel Out

When you practise Feel Out you become intimate with the universe of the body, the many different flavours, locations and intensities of body sensations. You do this by directing your attention on and over your whole body to any kind of physical-body sensations, including smells and tastes. These could be pleasant (delicious food, sensuous touch), neutral (breathing, pulse, bladder, muscles working, contact with clothes or chair, wind on skin) or unpleasant (itches, aches, pressures, muscle tensions, fatigue, hunger, bad odours). Note that by this definition, focusing on the breath is a subset of Feel Out. You can let your attention float among different types of sensations or control where and on what type of sensation you focus. For example, if your back or knees are sore, but the rest of you is comfortable, you could direct your attention away from the discomfort to other neutral or pleasant body sensations (contact on chair) or direct your attention to the uncomfortable sensations, pouring openness and acceptance into your noting. When practising with Feel Out, you are not conducting a mental inventory of body parts. You are making direct sensory contact with the body. Sometimes you will detect a slight tingly sensation that lets you know this contact has occurred.

FEEL OUT PRACTICE

1   Direct your attention on and over your whole body or to any particular part of your body, including physical-body sensations, touch, smell and taste.

2   Whenever you're aware of a physical-body sensation, note "Feel Out."

3   If all or part of that sensation drops away, and you happen to notice it, note "Gone."

See Out

When you practise See Out, you can gradually turn the banal act of sight into vision, developing the eye of the artist who sees nature deeply, the lover who sees beauty in the beloved or the engineer who perceives intricate details. At the deepest level, this can create the experience of merging with the sights, so that there is no you seeing, just the sunset, mountain, flower or person's face.

You do this by directing your attention continuously to external sights, letting your attention shift around as you will, exploring deeply whatever you are seeing. These images could be pleasant (a bed of flowers), neutral (a blank wall) or even unpleasant (clutter or grime).

SEE OUT PRACTICE

1 With your eyes open, direct your attention toward external sights. Let your line of sight float freely from direction to direction or object to object or place to place within an object.

2 Each time your line of sight shifts (whether spontaneous or intended), note "See Out."

3 If, when your line of sight shifts, you happen to notice the preceding sight drop away, note "Gone."

Hear Out

When you practise Hear Out, you can deeply tune in to the sounds you are hearing, the rising and falling in tone, the changes in rhythm or pulse. At the deepest level, this can create the experience of merging with the sound, where there is no you listening to the sound, just the sound itself.

You do this by directing your attention continuously to external sounds, whether occurring naturally (birds, traffic, machinery, conversation) or those you have selected (instrumental soundtrack). Again, these sounds could be pleasant, neutral or unpleasant for you.

HEAR OUT PRACTICE

1 Direct your attention toward your ears. Let your hearing float freely in all exterior directions as you listen to the sounds both up close and further away.

2 Whenever you become aware of a sound, note "Hear Out."

3　If all or part of a sound drops away, and you happen to notice it, note "Gone."

Focus Out on All

This is a global practice, including all objective sensations of the body, sight and sound. A Focus Out practice session could start with three to five minutes each of Feel Out, See Out and Hear Out, then, once you are sensitized to each of these spaces, could finish with several minutes of Focus Out on all spaces.

FOCUS OUT ON ALL PRACTICE

1　Let your attention float between physical-body sensations, sights and sounds. Work with whatever is available. If more than one is available at any one time, just choose one to note.

2　Note according to what you are paying attention to, "Feel Out," "See Out" or "Hear Out."

3　If something that you are focusing on suddenly drops away, and you happen to notice it, note "Gone."

Create Mindful Moments with Focus Out

While you can learn the basics of Focus Out or drill down deeply in formal seated practice, this method is also well suited to bringing mindfulness into moments throughout your day. These are examples of how you can do this using Focus Out techniques. Mix it up to suit yourself:

- During sports of any kind, Focus Out. Feel Out for any physical-body sensations, focusing on minute posture adjustments; See Out for anything visual around you (your golf ball, your surroundings as you run); Hear Out for any ambient sounds (the whack of the tennis ball).

- While walking, either outside or even down the hall at the office, Focus Out. Feel Out (your feet on the floor); See Out (the passing cubicles); Hear Out (the hum around you).

- While eating, Focus Out on the sensations relevant to enjoying your meal. Feel Out the tastes on your tongue; Hear Out the crunch of food in your mouth or ambient sounds around you; See Out for the appearance of the food on the plate.

- While listening to others, See Out to attend to all the cues of body language; Hear Out to bring continuous attention to the words and inferred meaning being spoken.

- While listening to music, either live or through earbuds, Hear Out to discern the different instruments or voices. Note "Gone" for the endings or sudden dropping away of sounds.

- While watching scary movies, See Out to practise equanimity skills. (I do this a lot!)

- While in a low-demand situation (a boring movie, on the bus, keeping an eye on the kids), See Out to explore the visual world for details that usually escape you.

- While in a noisy environment, Hear Out to tune in to the various sounds around you, discerning their differences, bringing equanimity to what was jarring.

Focus In

If, as Socrates said, knowing yourself is the essence of wisdom, then Focus In provides a window through which to view your inner, subjective experience so that you can fine-tune that knowing. In contrast to Focus Out, with Focus In you direct your attention inward to the emotional-body sensations, mental images and mental talk that make up your core subjective sense of self. Focus In is a powerful method. You may find it challenging; you may not always want to practise it. You may choose to make it a short component of a longer practice session, for example, a twenty-minute practice session could be ten minutes of Focus Out, then five minutes of Focus In and finish with five minutes of breath. But I highly recommend that, at some point, you make Focus In part of your mindfulness method repertoire.

When you Focus In, you do not try to change yourself. You clearly observe yourself, just as you are, with as much equanimity as you can manage. When you explore inside, you may discover yourself in layers. This can be like slowly lowering the water line that surrounds an iceberg, revealing what was already there but previously hidden. More mundanely, you can think of it as cleaning out a long-ignored closet.

At first, you discover the world of DAN, the inner chatter or mental images that are rattling around in your brain. They may not be particularly meaningful. Your brain may just be doing a random scan of readily accessible data. However, this does reveal the thinking that you didn't know you were thinking. Techniques like Feel In are the bases for interventions such as Mindfulness-Based Cognitive Therapy, with which you discover what you are thinking, then question it. Is it really true? Is it helpful or limiting? With Feel In, you also discover the self-reinforcing patterns that govern your moods, the inner thermostat that regulates your relatively constant happiness set point and bolsters innate traits of optimism or pessimism. By witnessing these unconscious patterns, you have the opportunity to adjust them.

You may also discover deeper subjective states. These could include old memories, difficult emotions or urges toward unhealthy behaviour. This is the world of shadow material, experiences that were so powerful that, at the time, all you could do was put them in storage. (The psychological term is denial or repression.) While some people do combine mindfulness practice with therapy, my own experience—and that of many clients—is more mundane. I have never experienced brand-new material or deeply repressed memories. I have revisited old wounds. At the time they were partially healed; now they can resurface again to be fully healed by the fresh air of awareness.

Focus In can be a powerful discovery and healing method. First, like any observational technique, when you consciously look *at* patterns that you were unconsciously looking *through*, you gradually disidentify from them. They lose their holding grip on you. Second, Focus In helps you deal with material that could otherwise be overwhelming, by breaking large chunks down into manageable pieces. If a strong emotion or dominant thought pattern comes up, you pour attention into its component parts: emotional-body sensations, inner word-streams and mental images. Like unravelling the threads in a knot, it is much easier to deal with each component singly than with the intertwined mass. Third, you significantly develop your mindfulness skills by staying focused on your interior experience (concentration), detecting subtle thinking or feelings (clarity) and greeting them all with openness and acceptance (equanimity).

With Focus In, you explore the emotional-body sensations, mental images and mental talk that contribute to your constructed self. I will review how to practise with each of the individual subcomponents and then collectively.

Feel In

Feel In refers to any body sensations that you judge, at that time, to be emotional in nature. This could be a rapid heartbeat, a clenched jaw, a furrowed brow, a fluttering stomach, a spontaneous smile, a sensation of warmth around the heart. What you are trying to do is become familiar with the somatic core of emotions that live in the body. (Just where did you think emotions lived anyway?) Detecting the relevant sensations is a matter of judgment and will involve some guessing and groping on your part. Note that you could judge the same feeling differently at different times. A rapid heartbeat could be due to a good run—in which case it would be Feel Out—or to an emotion such as fear—which would be Feel In.

In my view, this little box of Feel In as depicted on the Detailed Grid of Sensory Experience is the most potent of all. Working with Feel In, we can access our most basic emotions. Some of these emotional patterns go back to infancy, years before our capacity for reason evolved. The emotional intelligence literature is replete with references to an "amygdala hijack." This describes an immediate emotional response directed by the limbic brain out of proportion to the stimulus. It is triggered by an emotional pattern or threat and overwhelms the rational thinking functions of the neocortex. With Feel In, you may be working with emotions that are deeply wired in you. But wired does not necessarily mean permanent.

Please be careful and caring of yourself when you work with Feel In. Emotions may arise and you may have no idea why they are there. This is not the time to try and figure them out. Just bring equanimity to the sensations as best you can. If the emotional sensation is very strong, focus only on a small part of it. Or, if it is too strong, then bail out and practise something else. But the rewards for emotional self-awareness are immense. When you become intimate with emotional-body sensations, you will be increasingly able to discern emotions as they arise in you, know what triggers them, sit with them as they ebb and flow and become more able to express your emotions cleanly and skillfully.

Feel In emotional-body sensations may not always be present or available to you. If they are, this is the practice to follow.

FEEL IN PRACTICE

1   Direct your attention to feeling space, on and over your whole body.

2   Whenever you're aware of a body sensation that you judge to be emotional in nature, note "Feel In."

3   If all or part of that sensation drops away, and you happen to notice it, note "Gone."

See In

We usually consider sensory experience as having to do with the body and five senses, not with our thinking. But we *can* locate our thoughts, which occur literally in our heads. When you direct your attention to the space inside your head, you will find that you can detect internal mental images and internal mental talk. Together, mental images and mental talk describe how we can contact our thinking process in real time, as moment-by-moment sensory experiences. But it helps to know where to look.

For the visual component of thinking, look into what we will call "image space." This is most readily done with eyes closed. Place your attention within your head, slightly behind your eyes, where you can contact an internal mental screen, like an interior computer monitor or smartphone screen. You may be able to detect images on this interior mental screen. The images may be sharp or blurry, stable or fleeting, with clear or fuzzy content. Sometimes images may be available, other times not. People who are visual thinkers often find it easy to contact image space. (Not me.) When you work with image space, remember that you are not trying to track every single image that comes up, which would be impossible. You are simply making contact with visual thinking.

See In images may not always be present or available to you. If they are, this is the practice to follow.

SEE IN PRACTICE

1   Direct your attention to image space, within your head, slightly behind your eyes.

2   Whenever you're aware of a mental image, note that as "See In."

3   If all or part of an image drops away, and you happen to notice it, note "Gone."

Hear In

For the auditory component of thinking, direct your attention into what we will call "talk space." This is inside your head, roughly between your ears; like having an interior speaker. It's located a little further back in the head from image space. You will almost always be able to detect interior talking. This may be in the form of distinct words or indistinct verbal babble. The words may occur in a non-stop stream of sentences or intermittently. Remember that when you work with talk space, you are not engaging in an internal debate with yourself. That would just be more thinking! You are simply noting verbal thinking as it comes up, like sitting on the bank of a river watching as the bubbles or debris float by.

HEAR IN PRACTICE

1   Direct your attention to talk space, within your head, in the area roughly between your ears.

2   Whenever you're aware of mental talk, note that as "Hear In."

3   If all or part of mental talk drops away, and you happen to notice it, note "Gone."

Focus In on All

This is a global practice in which you include all subjective emotional-body sensations and the visual and auditory components of thinking in your focus range. As this may be new territory for you, it may take you some time to discern subtler content, such as visual thinking or emotional-body sensations. Even when your clarity and detection skills improve, not all of this content is always present. So you may find yourself practising the global version of Focus In on All quite a lot, working with whatever of Feel In-See In-Hear In is available at the time.

FOCUS IN ON ALL PRACTICE

1   Let your attention float between emotional-body sensations, mental images and mental talk. Work with whatever is available. If more than one is available at any one time, just choose one to note.

2   Note according to what you are paying attention to, "Feel In," "See In" or "Hear In."

3   If something that you are focusing on suddenly drops away, and you happen to notice it, note "Gone."

Unpacking Emotions with Feel In

While Focus Out is well suited to practising mindful moments throughout the day, Focus In, especially at first, is easier in formal practice while you are seated on a chair or cushion. When we experience strong emotions, we can often feel overwhelmed. Our amygdala responds instantly; our body reacts. How can you move beyond this? You can reduce overwhelm by breaking down an emotion into its component parts, dealing with each one separately. What we normally refer to as "a feeling" actually has two parts: the emotional sensations in the body and the thinking associated with those emotional sensations. Being able to unpack the components of emotions is unbelievably helpful in dealing with them. When you can move beyond instant emotional reaction, you give yourself a chance for a more considered response, bringing mind, body and heart to bear.

Here are two examples of working with Focus In to discern and unpack emotions.

The first example is for general exploration during a mindfulness practice session. You direct your attention over your whole body and into the interior of your head, intending to start off systematically, working with whatever becomes available. So you start with feel space, placing attention on your body. But, since you can't detect any emotional-body sensation, you quickly move on. You proceed to direct your attention on to image space, looking at your internal mental screen. You do detect some images, some banal and some in particular of the noisy neighbour in the upstairs apartment. "See In." You try to bring equanimity, even though the images are of you marching upstairs and yelling at the idiot. So you speak the labels out loud for a few moments, intentionally bringing an even-handed tone to your voice. "See In." Then you move on to talk space, inside your head. You do detect commentary, some of it boring and some of it a reaction to your neighbour. "Hear In." You know your emotions are engaged now, so you go back and revisit feel space to see if you can detect any emotional flavours in the body. Sure enough, there is tension in your jaw. "Feel In." You are now aware of tension that you did not realize was there. After about five minutes, you decide this has been enough of a workout, so you give yourself a cool down with Focus Out on body sensations.

The second example of using Focus In is to deal with a specific emotion that arose during the day. Let's say you have had an argument with your partner, another version of an argument you've had many times before. During your usual evening mindfulness session, you decide to deal with it. The instant you sit down, the voice in your head explodes. "Hear In." This time you speak the labels out loud, using a calm tone of voice, trying to induce equanimity in a painful situation. Then you redirect your attention to your body. You detect emotional sensations in many locations in your body, a tightening in your chest, around your eyes and in your hands. Your heartbeat seems fast. "Feel In." It's all you can do to stay with Feel In and Hear In, so you don't even bother investigating See In. After a while, you notice different flavours of emotions: anger, sadness and even a certain gladness (that comes from the conviction you are right). You notice that certain thought patterns lead to these distinct emotional-body sensations. Since you cannot tone down the inner volume in your head, you bring attention to all the different emotions coursing through the body, bringing as much equanimity as you can. "Feel In." After about ten minutes, you notice more calm in the body and a lower volume in the head. Later that evening, you notice a little less edge in your tone of voice with your partner. By facing your emotions, you have diminished their potential to surprise and overwhelm you. As a result, perhaps you projected less.

Focus on Rest

Have you ever imagined that mindfulness is all about mellowing out and enjoying blissful states? Focus on Rest can provide access to those kind of experiences. While Focus Out and Focus In direct attention to what is actively occurring in your outer and inner worlds, Focus on Rest directs attention to what is relatively inactive in your outer and inner worlds. Focus on Rest gives you a roadmap for various kinds of restful states that are pleasant, subtle and—once you know where to look—always available.

Noticing and tuning in to naturally occurring restful sensations is relaxing and inherently pleasant. It provides a great antidote to stress and can help you generate moments of calm throughout the day. Because it can feel so good, you are more likely to practise more often than you otherwise would, creating a positive feedback loop that is self-reinforcing and helps you build a sustainable mindfulness practice.

Restful states occur naturally all the time, but they are in the background of our awareness. As human beings we are wired to be alert to active signals in our environment: the tiger jumping out of the bush, the storm on the horizon, the car swerving around the corner or the client's frown. Focus on Rest orients you to subtler signals. It's like when you listen to music; at first you may not hear the drumbeat, but once you do, you realize how it permeates the song. Once you attune to the subtle rhythms of restful states, you realize you can tap in to them whenever you want or need.

With Focus on Rest, you direct attention to restful experiences in your body and in visual and auditory worlds. I will review how to practise with each of these subcomponents and then the global practice of Focus on Rest.

Feel Rest

In the physical body, feelings of rest can include: the muscles in the back relaxing as you settle into a posture; the diaphragm releasing in the end of every exhale; a sense of release or tranquility in those parts of the body that are not actively working, such as hands lying tranquilly on your lap. In the emotional body, a feeling of rest refers to a calm neutral state in which emotions are not coursing through you. When you are doing Feel Rest, not every part of you will be restful. Many parts of you will be active.

You are still actively breathing, digesting, pumping blood and holding yourself erect. You direct attention to those parts of you that *are* restful, leaving the more active states in the background. Sometimes these active states will be quite minimal, other times they may involve several parts of your body. Restful feelings will always be available to you, however, such as the muscle releasing on the exhale.

With Feel Rest, as well as noting restful states that are naturally present, you can also intentionally induce restful states by stretching up, then releasing the shoulders as you settle into your posture; by intentionally tightening then relaxing individual body parts; by breathing into emotional sensations to soothe them.

FEEL REST PRACTICE

1 Direct your attention on and over your whole body, both the objective natural functioning of the body and the subjective body, where you often detect emotional-body sensations.

2 When you are aware of rest in some part of your body, note "Feel Rest." This could be physical relaxation or emotional tranquility.

3 Sometimes a tangible sensation of rest may drop away; if so, you can note "Gone."

See Rest

Humans and birds of prey are the two animals that rely most on their vision. With See Rest, you let go of this strong orientation. You can do See Rest with eyes open or with eyes closed.

With eyes open, you disengage from sights and forms and intentionally defocus your gaze, becoming more aware of light and colour. (In martial arts, this can be referred to as "far mountain gazing" or "spirit eyes.") With eyes closed, you look at what you see behind your closed eyelids, which I will call a "grey-scale blank." This is usually some mixture of darkness or brightness. It may be uniform or mottled. For some people, the grey-scale blank version of See Rest is readily available; others may find it more challenging or perceive only a small corner of grey-scale blank.

SEE REST PRACTICE

1   Direct your attention to your head, to the area slightly behind your closed eyes. With your eyes closed, focus on the grey-scale blank that you see behind your eyelids. Or with your eyes open, defocus your gaze and focus on a diffuse sense of colour and light.

2   When you are aware of rest in some part of your visual field, note "See Rest."

3   If you are focusing on the grey-scale blank, you may notice patches of darkness or brightness disappear; if so, you can note "Gone."

Hear Rest

Sometimes, when you go from a noisy location to a quiet one, you can almost taste the silence. Hear Rest gives you a way to notice this on a regular basis. With Hear Rest, you direct your attention toward auditory states in both your outer and inner worlds.

Directing your attention outward, you may detect silence in the environment around you. There is unlikely to be complete silence (unless you're in a soundproof chamber), but you can check whether you detect silence in any direction. For example, by directing your attention inward, you may first notice your interior mental chatter. However, there are moments when this chatter spontaneously stops or pauses. If this happens and you should notice, this is an example of auditory rest.

HEAR REST PRACTICE

1   Direct your attention to the area between and around your ears.

2   If you are aware of the absence of sound in any direction around you, note that as "Hear Rest." If you are aware of the absence of inner mental talk, note that also as "Hear Rest."

3   If any part of Hear Rest drops away, and you happen to notice it, note "Gone."

Focus on All Rest

This is a global practice in which you include all available restful states: Feel Rest in the physical and emotional bodies, See Rest in the outer world and inner visual thinking and Hear Rest in exterior silence or inner mental quiet. Intentionally creating or becoming aware of subtly present restful states can be utterly delicious, like tapping in to a peacefulness you didn't know you had in you. Since restful experiences are subtle and may not be available in all spaces, you may find yourself practising the global version of Focus on Rest frequently. Remember that one or two restful states are always available to you: the grey-scale blank when your eyes are closed—See Rest—and the sense of release at the end of each exhale—Feel Rest. We will call this particular combination of restful states "Easy Rest." Like an instant refresher, you can call on Easy Rest whenever you need.

FOCUS ON ALL REST PRACTICE

1   Let your attention float between restful physical- or emotional-body sensations, a defocused gaze (eyes open) or grey-scale blank (eyes closed) of visual rest and the exterior silence or inner quiet of auditory rest.

2   Note, accordingly, "Feel Rest," "See Rest" or "Hear Rest." If restful states in all three spaces are available, use the label "All Rest."

3   If a rest you are noting drops away, and you happen to notice it, note "Gone."

Focus on Rest to Help You Sleep

If you don't always sleep well—thirty percent of adults experience symptoms of insomnia—then Focus on Rest can help. This is an example of mindfulness practised while you are lying down, which you can do as you go to bed or if you wake in the night.

When we can't sleep, the first thing most of us do is worry. "Oh no, I've got to get to sleep or I'll be a wreck tomorrow." This just winds us up even tighter. So reframe this worry by recognizing that while you cannot control getting a good night's sleep, you can get a good night's rest. Then begin to practise Focus on Rest. Create relaxation by lifting and releasing your shoulders or by clenching and releasing your brow. Tune in to the relaxation in the body and the release of each exhale as you lie on your comfortable mattress. "Feel Rest." Gaze at the grey-scale blank behind your closed eyes. "See Rest." Notice the silence all around you. "Hear Rest." Appreciate the restfulness, even if it is not leading to sleep.

Here is a short example of how this might work.

You fall asleep quickly, but then wake at 2:30 a.m. You find yourself worrying; impending layoffs at work, a child in trouble at school. At first, you do your usual tossing and turning, but after a few minutes you decide to give Focus on Rest a try. You shift your posture to your favourite sleeping position and begin the practice. You can detect the worry-wart monologue in your head, so as an antidote you decide to listen externally. The house is mostly quiet, except for the hum of the furnace. "Hear Rest... Hear Rest..." You luxuriate in this exterior silence for several minutes. Then you turn your attention to your body. There are some tensions and fidgety sensations, but you look elsewhere—for physical relaxation in the body. Your back and arms are relaxed. "Feel Rest... Feel Rest..." You induce a little more physical relaxation by tightening then releasing the legs. "Feel Rest... Feel Rest..." You do feel less agitated now, so you see whether you can hold both kinds of restful experiences at once, the exterior silence and the interior rest. "Feel and See Rest..." You can do this, but you decide it feels too much like work, so you just stay with the delicious silence. "Hear Rest..." You pass some time like this, after a while stop the intentional labelling and find yourself drifting off to sleep. You wake to your morning alarm, discovering you're reasonably refreshed.

Focus on Flow

When you look at many objects—a table, a tree trunk, a person's body—they seem to be solid and stable. Yet all these seemingly solid objects are composed of atoms and molecules in constant motion. So you know conceptually that what you observe depends on the perspective and scale. Focus on Flow helps you observe the dynamic or energetic aspects that may be detectable in any experience. Focus on Flow is a direct experience of the constant flow of change that is part of our universe.

Why would this matter to you? Because the experience can be fascinating, like the depths of your being receiving a massage. Because, if you are experiencing something unpleasant, you can say with confidence "this too *is* passing" (not this too *shall* pass). Because it normalizes in your entire being what you know in your head: Change is constant and not necessarily something to fear. Because, as you learn to surf in flow, you directly experience that you are not as fixed as you thought you were. You develop confidence in your resilient ability to adapt to change.

During mindfulness practice, the experience of flow states may or may not be available to you. (I will give examples of these flow-state experiences below.) For some people, they are easily accessible, for others not so much. Or you may find detecting flow is easily accessible in certain spaces more than others (for example, body flow). Please do not feel that you ought to make this happen or be able to practise it. However, it's helpful to have a way to notice flow should it occur.

When you direct attention to any kind of experience, you may find that it is stable or that it has a kind of movement in it. If it is stable, enjoy the sensation of timeless groundedness, like an eternal "now." But if you detect some kind of movement, you can choose Focus on Flow. This movement could be any kind of dynamic or changing aspect of outer, inner or restful experiences. Flow experiences may be obvious or subtle, they may be pleasant or uncomfortable. You can expect a certain amount of guesswork as you learn to discern the different flavours of flow. With Focus on Flow, you explore each or all of your flow sensations in body, visual or auditory experience. I will review how to practise with each of these individual subcomponents and then practise collectively.

Feel Flow

Feel Flow pertains to any kind of change in your objective body or your subjective emotional-body sensations. The possible range is large: breath in and out, stomach gurgling, blood pulsing, inward or outward pressures on muscles or skin, spreading or collapsing of any physical sensation, increase or decrease in intensity or frequency of any somatic sensation, a deep sense of vibration or undulation and so on.

FEEL FLOW PRACTICE

1   Direct your attention to somatic space, including any of objective physical-body sensations, subjective emotional-body sensations or restful body sensations.

2   Whenever you're aware of a change, pressure, movement or force, you may choose to note that as "Feel Flow."

3   If all or part of this movement drops away, that is a moment to note "Gone."

See Flow

Visual flow can occur in outer, inner or restful experience. With your eyes closed, if you see mental images, they may move, morph, melt or become animated. The grey-scale blank behind your closed eyes may swirl or appear pixelated. With your eyes open, the colour or form of solid objects may become wavy; if you defocus your gaze, the light may appear to swirl. These are all examples of visual flow.

SEE FLOW PRACTICE

1   Direct your attention to visual space, including outer, inner or restful sensations.

2   Whenever you're aware of any kind of visual movement, flow or change, note "See Flow."

3   If all or part of this flow drops away, note "Gone."

Hear Flow

Auditory flow can occur in outer, inner or restful experience. Listening out, you may detect an increase or decrease in volume of sound, a speeding up or a slowing down. Listening in to your mental talk, you may detect it getting louder or softer, gripping you, spreading throughout your head. You may detect a subtle undercurrent or hum in talk space that is noise but not yet words. All these are examples of auditory flow.

HEAR FLOW PRACTICE

1   Direct your attention to auditory space, including outer or inner sensations.

2   Whenever you're aware of any kind of auditory fluctuation, flow or change, note "Hear Flow."

3   If all or part of this flow drops away, note "Gone."

Focus on All Flow

This is a global practice in which you include all available flow states: Feel Flow in the physical and emotional bodies, See Flow in outer sights and inner mental images and Hear Flow in exterior sounds or inner mental talk. Focusing on all flow states can loosen your sense of inner rigidity, like receiving a whole-person massage that breaks up the kinks in your being. Since flow states are subtle and may not be available in all spaces, you may find the global version quite accessible.

FOCUS ON ALL FLOW PRACTICE

1   Let your attention float between fluctuating, changing or flowing experiences in somatic, visual or auditory spaces.

2   Note, accordingly, "Feel Flow," "See Flow" or "Hear Flow."

3   If all or part of any flow experience drops away and you happen to notice it, note "Gone."

Working with Flow to Handle Discomfort

Mindfulness practices can be used to handle a wide range of discomforts and pain, as we saw with Alex's story of recovering from PTSD in Chapter 2. Knowing you have methods to cope with pain can contribute significantly to your resilience muscle of handling unpleasant feelings. This is a short personal example of my coping with aching knees. It illustrates multiple strategies for acknowledging and dealing with discomfort, including the use of Feel Flow.

I am participating in a half-day meditation program that has a number of timed sits interspersed with Q&As. For the first period, I sit cross-legged on the floor and feel fine. For the second period, I change my position to sit in a chair. For the third period, I sit cross-legged on the floor again. I know my knees will ache, but I decide to face the discomfort. I have no serious medical issues with my knees and know that once I stand up, I will feel fine. I decide to approach this like a short, intense workout, the kind now advocated by high-performance athletic coaches. For twenty-five minutes, I will not budge my legs.

When I first experience the dull aching of the knees, I decide to focus away from the discomfort. I let it be there, but in the background. In the foreground, I Focus on Rest. Tuning in to the body, I notice the arms and shoulders are relaxed. "Feel Rest..." The jaw is relaxed. "Feel Rest..." Tuning in to outside the body, I hear the silence all around. "Hear Rest..." This works well and for a few minutes I don't notice the discomfort. But soon, perhaps now that some attention is directed toward auditory space, I hear angry mental talk in my head. "Stupid knees. Everyone else seems to be okay. Why me? Will this ever get better?" So now I decide to focus directly on the discomfort by practising Focus In, dissecting the components of my reaction to the discomfort. So I direct attention to the body. Are there any emotional flavours present? Yes, anger in the chest, sadness around the eyes and fear around the lower belly. "Feel In..." Is there any inner thinking? Yes, mental images from the first childbirth. "See In..." Any inner talk? Yes: "Why does this hurt so much? I'm scared." "Hear In..." After several minutes of Focus In, I realize that I've been so busy there, I haven't paid much attention to my knees lately. So I redirect my attention to the knees. The discomfort level seems to have dialled down a bit. I can detect a distinct pulsing. (Maybe blood flow?) I decide to interpret this movement as flow and stay with Feel Flow for several more minutes. How far does this flow sensation extend? At the farthest extent, midway up the thighs, this tingling flow sensation is almost neutral. Certainly the small core of pressure around the kneecap isn't so bad. "Feel Flow..." Then I notice that the emotional sensations in the chest and belly area seem to be swirling around, too. "Feel Flow..." The bell rings and I slowly stretch out my legs. Somehow, I feel looser all over, like someone has put WD-40 into my joints!

[9]

Practices to Transcend and Nurture Positive in Self and World

---

I N T H E last two chapters, you learned several mindfulness practices to help you Appreciate Self and World. With Feel-See-Hear, you heightened moment-by-moment sensory awareness (MoMo), learning to experience yourself and the world around you with radical richness. With the Feel-See-Hear variation techniques—Focus Out, Focus In, Focus on Rest and Focus on Flow—you discerned unique patterns in your experience and learned practical tools, such as coping with difficult emotions or accessing restorative rest when you need it.

All the practices of the Appreciate-Self-and-World type occur on the left-hand or downward slope of the U curve of personal change. With MoMo, you redirect your awareness of familiar phenomena in a new way, disidentifying from the autopilot patterns of DAN (default attentional network). By becoming aware of yourself and your habitual reactions, you are able to let them go. You can now see ways of thinking and being that were previously unconscious, such as your blind spots and assumptions.

But, at some point, you have to move on from this letting go phase. You have to start developing the new—and navigating the awkward transition zone in between. This is precisely what the next two methods do: Transcend Self and World and Nurture Positive in Self and World.

Mindfulness Helps You to Touch Transcendence

The problem most of us encounter with personal learning and change—whether recovering from trauma, grieving a loss or adapting to a new challenge—is that we cut short the process. We try to move quickly from the old to the new. We let go—a bit. We experience some of our difficult emotions. We examine our surface assumptions. But we don't go all the way. We don't go deep.

Usually, we do whatever we can at the time to cope, then move on with our life. (When my brother died I was in shock, then I felt grief. It was only later that I could taste anger, regret and fear.) It's like we go halfway down the U curve then jump across, without going all the way to the bottom. Which is too bad, because the bottom of the U is where you find treasure.

Letting Go of
the Old through
Appreciate
Self and World
practices

Letting
Come the
New through
Nurture Positive
practices

Gap of Transition through
Transcend practices

The dot at the bottom of the U curve represents the transition zone. This is the gap between old and new. It can be an awkward place. But if you know how to navigate here, you can find your way through to the other side.

This is the place where you don't have the comfort of automatically acting in the old ways but have not yet found new ones. You have questions but not yet answers. You know what is wrong, but you don't yet know what is right. It is a gap. An open space of possibility. Possibility because what is truly new never comes from the old but from a space in between the old and the new. We hear this in our folk wisdom: "When one door closes, another one opens." True. But what you don't hear about is the corridor between the two doors. Knowing how to be in this transitional space offers the possibility for real transformation, for genuinely new capabilities, not just a reworking of the same old ones.

You may think this kind of transcendence is rare or requires special powers. Not necessarily. What it does require is practice of certain skills. You need to become comfortable with moving toward the edges of what you can detect with your senses or your conceptual mind, with discerning deeper underlying patterns, with accepting the unknown. It's like the medieval mariners' maps with inscriptions like "Here be dragons" on the farthest edges of the known oceans, beyond which lay unknown worlds. The mindfulness methods of the Transcend type can help you approach the unknown without being afraid of dragons.

You have already learned some of these skills. Heightened momentary awareness (MoMo) achieved by practising the Feel-See-Hear methods develops the skill of exploring right to the edges of what you can detect with your senses. The varied methods of Focus Out, Focus In, Focus on Rest and Focus on Flow help you discern deeper, subtler patterns in how you approach and respond to the world. Now I will give you two additional methods that directly address the space of transition and transcendence.

Just Note Gone picks up the optional label of "Gone" from the Feel-See-Hear methods and asks you to focus on what I call "vanishings" and endings: these are moments when elements of perception disappear from your experience. This acclimatizes you to the constant micro-endings happening all around you. Like the end of an exhale. Or the end of this sentence. When you know how to detect and accept small endings during meditation, you can bring these skills to navigating the larger endings in your life.

Do Nothing asks you to drop all intentions to control your attention and just rest in awareness. It is the ultimate in restful experience. While other methods ask you to actively reach out to explore your sensory universe, Do Nothing asks you to wait receptively for the universe to reach out and touch you.

Just Note Gone

In the United Kingdom—and in my own city—there is a well-known sign in subway stations, "Mind the Gap," alerting passengers to the slight gap between the train door and the station platform. Just Note Gone is all about minding the gaps in your sensory experience. You learn to notice the edges of your senses by paying attention to anything in sensory experience that drops away or vanishes. Such as a burst of mental talk. Or an external sound. Or a body sensation. Just Note Gone is one way of experiencing the Buddhist concept of impermanence in a practical, positive way. When you are accustomed to normal, everyday "Gones," then you are more able to handle life's big "Gones."

If you should find the experience distressing, then don't practise Just Note Gone. But for many people, the experience of "Gone-ness" is strangely rewarding, yielding a sense of restfulness and richness. I believe there are several reasons for this.

As moments of "Gone" are not always obvious, you need fairly well-developed mindfulness skills to detect them. At this stage, the experience of concentration, clarity and equanimity in themselves are inherently rewarding.

At the psychological level, "Gones" in your internal mental images or internal mental talk point to momentary cessations in your thinking process. (The voice of DAN.) This gap gives you an opportunity to detect "the still, small voice" within. These gaps can lead to unexpected creative richness—a new idea, a personal insight, an intuition or an old idea now heard with new clarity. Perhaps the huge "Gone" of my brother's suicide helped me to hear an old idea, "You should meditate," with new force.

At the deepest spiritual level, "Gones" can lead to a sense of being pointed toward the source from which all things come and to which all things return. This occurs not as an idea but as a lived experience of both vacuity and richness. The moment of "Gone" is a true absence. Nothing is there. Yet it is usually brief; another experience arises shortly after. So working with "Gones," you may literally experience something arising from nothing.

How to Work with Just Note Gone

As the name implies, Just Note Gone is a noting technique with which you are focusing only on endings or vanishings in any or all of the Feel-See-Hear categories. "Gones" may or may not be available to you at any given time, so there is a certain opportunism in working with this method. If during your meditation practice you are already noticing "Gones," then you can decide to pursue this method. Or, you can investigate "Gones," such as external sights or sounds that come and go, if you are in an environment where they naturally occur.

Here is a list that illustrates where you can direct your attention to detect "Gones," using the external and internal portions of the Detailed Grid of Sensory Experience where "Gones" are most readily detectable:

- The dropping away of all or part of a physical-body sensation, for example, breath, pulse, heartbeat, muscle twinge, tension spasm

- The dropping away of all or part of an emotional-body sensation, for example, an ache or clenching that you deem to be emotional in nature

- The dropping away of all or part of a visual sight in the external world, for example, an object leaving your line of sight as you or as it moves, or as your eyes move around or over an object

- The dropping away of all or part of an internal visual image

- The dropping away of all or part of a sound in the external world, for example, the end of a sound, the end of a note of music

- The dropping away of all or part of internal mental talk, for example, the end of a burst of mental chatter

What drops away may be small or large, well defined or vague, long term or fleeting. It may come back again. If you have an emotional reaction to "Gone," you can note when that, too, is gone. You do not need to note every single instance of "Goneness," just keep your attention focused on moments of vanishing in your experience.

JUST NOTE GONE PRACTICE

1 Let your attention freely float among any or all body, visual or auditory experiences.

2 Whenever all or part of something drops away or drops off, and you happen to notice it, note "Gone."

Just Note Gone Can Be Surprising

When you are discussing techniques that touch transcendence, it is presumptuous to make predictions! But I do want to give you an example of how the Just Note Gone method can be applied.

Let's say you are doing your regular evening sit of fifteen minutes. It's been a stressful day and you just want to rest, so you intend to do the Focus on Rest technique. Just your luck! There's roadwork outside your apartment and they're making a heck of a lot of noise. How can you rest with that going on? You decide to abandon your plan and just deal with it by turning toward the challenge, listening directly to the sound of drilling. "Hear Out..." You label out loud for a few moments, using a calm tone of voice to induce equanimity. Then it dawns on you that the drilling is happening in spurts. There is an end to each burst of sound. "Hear Out... Hear Out... Gone... Hear Out... Gone..." This brings some relief.

You decide to follow up on this experience and do Just Note Gone in any of the Feel-See-Hear spaces. First, you direct your attention to auditory space, this time mostly outside to the sounds in the environment. There's the drill, of course, but also the furnace and your cat. You direct your attention to all these sounds, looking for any abrupt endings. There are plenty. The end of a burst of drilling, the end of a purring. "Gone..." Then you direct your attention to the body's somatic space. Any "Gones" here? The end of each exhale, of each inhale, of each pulse around the neck. "Gone..." Then you direct your attention to visual space, behind your closed eyelids. You see internal images quite readily, and now you find that you are able to notice the ending of some of these images. "Gone..."

After some minutes of this, you discover you have barely noticed that the drilling has stopped. You were busy paying attention to other little "Gones"! You find yourself quite relaxed, despite the stressful start. Right at the very end of your sit, an idea pops into you head about a problem with a work project that's been stymying you for weeks. You jot it down in your Notes app so you can discuss it with colleagues tomorrow. Something emerges from Just Note Gone. What a surprise!

Do Nothing

As a practice to contact transcendence, Do Nothing stands in stark contrast to Just Note Gone. With Just Note Gone, you bring strong intentions to actively noting subtle gaps in experience, bringing you to the very edges of what you as a human can experience with your senses. With Do Nothing, you drop intentions entirely, surrendering your attempts at control so that transcendence can reach out and touch you.

What might you experience when you Do Nothing? At one end, it could almost be the same as not meditating at all, just more of DAN on autopilot, with non-stop inner mental talk or mental images. You might feel very spacey or uncomfortably disoriented. If so, then don't do this method for now. At the other end, you could experience states that are very restful, with a sense of release or freedom. I believe there are several reasons for this.

Do Nothing is all about allowing. "Let whatever happens, happen." This cultivates the mindfulness skill of equanimity. Learning how to let go and let be can bring its own distinct taste of release.

You learn to detect where will and control reside in the body and to release some of these often-unconscious control mechanisms. When you practise "Do Nothing," there is still a lot of doing that will happen in you. All the functions of the autonomic nervous system continue: breathing, digestion, heart pumping, even sexual arousal. You do not intend for these functions to happen, they just do. But you may detect other phenomena that you didn't think were intentional and find you can drop them. For example, I experience an ongoing clenching in my right shoulder and neck. Sometimes I can drop them, sometimes I can't. But I did not know that my innate drive was so deeply embedded in me and has taken up residence all along the right side of my body! Becoming aware and able to let go of unconscious intentions can bring release and rest.

At the spiritual level, or for those of religious faith, Do Nothing is about opening to a greater presence. By detecting and surrendering your personal intentions to a larger will, you become a vehicle for spirit to move through you.

How to Work with Do Nothing

Do Nothing involves as little intention as possible. There are two important things to understand about the concept of intention. First, only things that you *can* drop are considered intentional, voluntary or within your control. If you cannot drop something, then by this definition it is not voluntary and is therefore not an intention. So if you find yourself thinking, and you can drop the intention to think, fine. But if a thought arises and you cannot drop it, that is also fine, because this thought is not a voluntary action. (It is quite humbling to experience how many of our thoughts happen to us rather than our intending to think them.) Second, this practice should involve no struggle or work. If you find yourself struggling to drop an intention, then you are practising an intention. Dropping means to let go of an intention in that moment. If it drops away easily, fine. If it doesn't, then leave it be. The outcome of this practice may feel like a deep meditation or like no meditation at all. Both are signs that you are doing it correctly. Whether or not you wish to practise this method is for you to decide.

You do not need to continuously monitor whether you are intending anything, for that itself would be an intention. You may notice your intention to control awareness frequently or only occasionally. Either is fine. But if you do happen to become aware of an intention, then drop it if you can. You may become aware of intentions in any of the Feel-See-Hear categories, for example, mental thoughts or images, body or muscle movements, emotional-body sensations. If you find yourself focused, centred or calm, fine. If you find that you want to maintain that state, drop that intention.

DO NOTHING PRACTICE

1 Let whatever happens, happen.

2 Whenever you are aware of an intention to control your attention, drop that intention.

Doing Nothing, in Practice and in Life

Here is an example of Do Nothing incorporated into a regular mindfulness practice. Let's say you are a go-getter, goal-focused kind of person. Even your friends have commented on your slightly obsessive tendencies! Life is pretty demanding, with constant interruptions at work and last-minute changes to the kids' sports schedules. So when you practise mindfulness, you like the constancy of a steady routine. Your favourite is Feel-See-Hear: Just Feel, Just See, Just Hear, then Note Everything, about five minutes each. With your natural curiosity, you like exploring what is available within each of these spaces. By halfway into your time, usually in the Just Hear section, you find yourself noticing more details. You hear soft sounds from down the hallway and wisps of inner mental talk. Your concentration and clarity are pretty good! But sometimes it just feels like work—more focus, more alertness. You realize you need to find ways to offset your automatic goal-focused orientation, your tendency to approach every problem with effort.

So you decide to add another five minutes on to your regular practice, three to four days a week. For this last five minutes, you will Do Nothing. You set a ringer on your timer for the last five minutes, to help you make this awkward switch. At first, it feels weird not to be applying effort. You're used to the rhythmic noting; you like the precision of the method and the vividness that results. Can anything else really be meditating? But now, when you notice an intention to note, you drop it. It's easy to drop the labelling part. Sometimes the noting falls away and you feel so scattered. But sometimes the rhythmic pulsing of noting seems to happen on its own. You are still enjoying being mindfully aware, but the experience seems fuzzier. Your attention wanders more, often into thinking. Often you cannot drop the thinking, but occasionally you can.

For the first few weeks of Do Nothing, you wonder what you're accomplishing. Then one day at work, you notice that you're slightly less irritated when things don't go as planned. You're able to bring some equanimity to fuzzy, chaotic situations. This reinforces your motivation to keep Do Nothing as part of your practice.

A few months later, you're having an argument with your young son about homework. Why can't he just put some effort into it? You recall the Do Nothing method, and for a few seconds during the argument, you drop all effort; you let go of your ideas of the right way to do it, of the proper outcomes. (You do not drop your love for him or your values around persistence.) Suddenly, you can see more deeply into his eyes; he looks like he's feeling trapped. You relax a bit. Maybe there is another way? How about thirty minutes of outdoor play then back to the homework?

Nurture Positive

Nurture Positive practices live on the right-hand, upward slope of the U curve, giving us methods to bring something new into being. Why is this the very last of all the techniques we cover? Not because it is the least important, and not because it is the last thing you should do. Indeed, some of my clients make Nurture Positive a centrepiece of their practice. (It has become increasingly central in my own practice.) From the perspective of learning and changing, though, this sequence makes sense. Through Appreciate Self and World practices based on Feel-See-Hear, we develop greater self-awareness and let go of old patterns. Through Transcend Self and World practices, we learn to detect and rest in the transition zone. Now, with Nurture Positive in Self and World practices, we are truly ready to embark on something new.

Nurture Positive is a suite of mindfulness methods that help you intentionally create your better self. You do this using the Feel-See-Hear categories you are already familiar with, but now actively creating the positive rather than neutrally observing what is. Paying attention to your positive intentions helps you to nurture them. You become habituated to these ideas; you lay down new neural networks. Of course, you can't just meditate yourself into a brand new you. You have to take new actions, too. The Practice Map of Conscious Living in Chapter 10 will show you how to integrate the groundwork of Nurture Positive with concrete new behaviours that help you embody your best intentions.

Nurture Positive is a reworking of many different kinds of practices that support becoming a better self. In the sports world, this is called the mental game. Athletes will clearly visualize both the tangible outcomes they are seeking and mental frames of mind they want to bring to their efforts. In the psychology world, this includes practices such as positive reframing, positive psychology, self-kindness, visualization or intention setting. In the spiritual or religious world, this includes compassion practices and prayer. The goal of Nurture Positive practices—some would say all meditation practice—is to become an admirable human being, according to your own inner lights and the best virtues of your society.

When you engage in Nurture Positive practices like visualization, your brain interprets the imagery as equivalent to real-life action. So while you cannot simplistically "think and grow rich," you can create new neural pathways through both mindfulness practice and real-life deeds that lead you toward your desires. For example, during turbulent family times, I visualize peaceful outcomes, practise better communication skills and add the occasional heartfelt prayer!

While the science is still young, Nurture Positive practices may utilize mind-body connections as demonstrated by the placebo effect. Placebos are inert substances used in clinical trials for new medications. Up to one in three people will experience a placebo effect after being given something as innocuous as a sugar pill. If a person believes they are taking a strong medicine, they may experience an improvement in symptoms, even though they were given a placebo. Expectations can work the other way, too, in what's called the "nocebo effect." If people are told of potential side-effects of a drug being trialled, they may experience these symptoms, even when taking a placebo. So however it works, creating and maintaining positive expectations can be very powerful.

There could be many reasons that motivate you to practise Nurture Positive. It could be for yourself or on behalf of others. It could be to foster specific characteristics or behaviours in yourself. It could be to extend positive feelings to others. You may want to extend some kindness to yourself while you are going through a rough patch. You may want to extend healing intentions to others who are hurting.

You may realize that you are not always living up to your espoused values, such as honesty, courage or kindness. Through Nurture Positive, you could visualize yourself behaving differently, hear yourself saying different words and contact the pleasant emotions that would come from being true to your values. Perhaps you are struggling with certain behaviours that aren't productive, such as nervous tension before a difficult conversation. Through your enhanced mindfulness skills, you're now aware that you tend to postpone making the call or soft-coat a difficult message or blurt out words without considering their impact on others. Through Nurture Positive, you could visualize the other person acting in a receptive, friendly way or imagine yourself acting with calm strength.

How to Work with Nurture Positive

With Nurture Positive, you are working with the same Feel-See-Hear categories used in Feel In, in other words, emotional-body sensations, mental imagery and mental talk. Instead of observing with equanimity, you now actively create positive emotional-body sensations, positive mental imagery and positive mental talk. You can then apply these to anything relevant to you, such as cultivating healthy emotions, rational thinking or productive behaviours.

Feel Good refers to the positive or higher emotions, such as interest, friendliness, joy, hope, gratitude, patience, compassion, forgiveness, love and so on. If you are able to readily contact or create these emotions, then you can start with Feel Good. If not, you may want to start with the positive mental thinking of See Good or Hear Good and then see what emotions result from that. Once you contact a positive emotion, you can intentionally spread that over your whole body.

See Good refers to creating positive internal mental images. These could be almost anything: a beautiful scene, someone you love or admire, a favourite pet, an ideal or iconic image, a fond memory, an ideal outcome or behaviour.

Hear Good refers to creating positive internal mental talk. This could be a short phrase that connects with a See Good image, positive self-talk, an affirmative phrase, a few words of prayer or mantra.

Here are some examples of how you might Nurture Positive for yourself and others, cultivating positive emotions, healthy thinking and productive behaviours through your mindfulness practice:

- Physically smile. Although it may feel artificial, the act of smiling is known to affect your mood and activate feel-good neurotransmitters in the brain.

- Notice if pleasant emotions are already present; if so, linger with them.

- Trigger positive emotional reactions through sights, sounds or tactile sensations that you enjoy, for example, gazing at a beautiful object or picture, recalling the face of a loved one, listening to your favourite music and contacting the pleasant feelings it evokes.

- Recall the many positive things in your life, which perhaps you take for granted, and see if you can contact a feeling of gratitude. Nurture this feeling with a suitable inner phrase, for example, "Thank you for…" (An everyday example of this is saying grace before a meal.)

- Cultivate a sense of compassion by visualizing a person (someone you know, or perhaps a stranger) and internally repeating positive phrases directed toward them. This is a secular reworking of Buddhist loving-kindness practices or religious prayer.

- If during your mindfulness practice you notice negative inner mental talk, you can choose to initially note it through Hear In, then change it with Nurture Positive. You could counter your inner critic through a phrase such as, "I am good enough." Or question compulsive tendencies with, "Is this thought really true?"

- Foster positive behaviour change by visualizing yourself acting differently—sinking your putt, closing the sale, speaking in public with confidence, hugging your sulking child, negotiating for win-win results.

You can work with any or all of Feel Good, See Good or Hear Good techniques that are available to you. You may have one that you prefer—or feel compelled to work on—or you may mix it up. Start working with whatever is easiest for you, whether that is wishing for world peace, visualizing a happier relationship or just sending yourself some kindness. Experiment over time to find what is most natural for you, then gradually extend the range of your concern.

NURTURE POSITIVE PRACTICE

1   Decide on which of Feel Good, See Good or Hear Good you'd like to work with.

2   Anchor yourself by tuning in to any pleasant emotional-body sensation, creating an appropriate mental image or repeating internally a short phrase.

3   Direct your emotional-body sensation, image or phrase in ways relevant to you, such as positive behaviour change, fulfilling relationships, healthy thinking patterns or emotional states you'd like to encourage.

Nurture Positive Examples

I find it's easiest to think of Nurture Positive as a suite of techniques that you can mix and match. Many people, myself included, like to include all three types of practice in a mindfulness session; start with any of the Feel-See-Hear or variant techniques in the Appreciate theme; then spend time with Just Note Gone or Do Nothing in the Transcend theme; then finish up with Nurture Positive. You can practise Nurture Positive during a period of seated meditation practice or during mindful moments in your day. You may use the same Nurture Positive practice every time or adapt it depending on what occurred earlier in the sit. You can give it a secular, spiritual or religious flavour, depending on your beliefs. You can make it general or situation specific.

Here are some examples of how you can combine these various possibilities:

Nurture Positive: Loving-Kindness

A loving-kindness meditation is the use of phrases that express caring and well wishes. The practice is often included in Mindfulness-Based Stress Reduction programs. You can find guided loving-kindness meditations, or make up your own. With Feel Good, See Good and Hear Good, you can amplify the classic practice to permeate your whole being. In the Buddhist traditions, you start out by sending well wishes to yourself, then expand the circles of care to include others. North Americans often have a hard time with this, so in this example I'll reverse the order. I'll also start out with See Good, but you can use whatever sequence works for you.

Start with See Good by visualizing someone or something that generates a positive emotion. It could be someone you love, a beautiful scene in nature, the memory of a childhood pet, a small act of kindness that you witnessed. Actively imagine this positive image in your mind's eye. Now add Feel Good by directing attention to the body, especially to locations where you know you tend to experience positive emotions, such as the heart area, or the mouth and jaw where you smile. Do you detect any positive emotions associated with the positive images? Perhaps you can just generate positive emotions at will. Now move to Hear Good by creating positive internal mental talk; a phrase that captures your positive intentions. Repeat this phrase internally to yourself, directing it at someone you care for. "May you be happy." Or, "May you know love, comfort, safety, freedom from illness or distress..." After a few minutes extend these well wishes more broadly, perhaps to people you know casually. "May you be well." If you wish, you can extend these positive intentions broadly to the whole state, country or globe. But don't forget yourself. Finish by extending to yourself the positive regard you wish for others. "May I be happy, peaceful, content…"

Nurture Positive: Productive Behaviours

Nurture Positive can also be used in specific ways to foster healthy thinking and productive behaviours. This could range from visualizing yourself being calm before a major exam, rehearsing the mental game before a golf tournament or just imagining happy chaos before a birthday party for six-year-olds. Here is an example of using Nurture Positive to help you prepare for a team presentation at which you know you will get some difficult questions. Inner preparation through mindfulness can complement your objective preparations such as developing presentation material and rehearsing for the Q&A.

For a few days before the team presentation, you make sure to do your daily mindfulness practice. Your inner talk is busy and your body is tense, but you tell yourself that you're coming into contact with your worry now, so it doesn't jump out at you on the big day. During your practice, you start with the general Feel-See-Hear method, then finish with Nurture Positive. When you do Nurture Positive, you start with See Good by visualizing the friendly faces of your colleagues. Then you imagine the faces of the client (or boss) reacting positively to your presentation. You imagine yourself responding to a curve-ball question with confidence and competence. Then you move to Feel Good. You know your team holds a positive message that will help carry the product forward, so you come in contact with your enthusiasm for what you are doing. This enthusiasm you can detect as a lightness in the chest area. Lastly, you move to Hear Good. You generate a short positive phrase that will support your positive intentions both now and later during the presentation itself. "May this work out for the best for everyone."

Nurture Positive can also be practised in mindful moments throughout the day. It can be a way to connect with others through our common humanity, to counteract our tendency to shut down in the face of suffering or to complement our positive acts of kindness and giving. The possibilities are endless, whether you internally repeat a phrase, wordlessly direct positive emotions or visualize positive actions. For example, you might say, "May you find what you need" as you pass a homeless person or "May you find shelter" to the victims of a natural disaster (as, perhaps, you also make a donation). You might silently direct compassion to a colleague who you know is stressed out at work and at home or visualize your shy child being quietly happy.

THIS COMPLETES your introduction to mindfulness methods. You now have a broad range to select from. With Feel-See-Hear practices you cultivate deep moment-by-moment awareness of sensory experiences. By appreciating deeply what is, you loosen the tug of default, unconscious patterns. With Feel-See-Hear variation practices, you delve deeply into the outer sensory world, your inner sense of self or subtle restful or flowing states. Practices like Just Note Gone or Do Nothing help you navigate the awkward transition zone between old patterns and new possibilities. Nurture Positive practices give you methods to intentionally nurture your better self. You can start with any practice that appeals, learn as many as you like or stick with your personal favourite. Since they all build the same mindful awareness skills of concentration, clarity and equanimity, don't let yourself be overwhelmed by choices. Regardless of which methods you choose, how do you find ways to integrate practice into your life? That is what we turn to next.

[10]

Integrating Mindfulness into Your Life

I F YOU'VE ever tried to implement a New Year's resolution, you know how hard it can be to develop a new healthy lifestyle habit. You may have sincere intentions, you may know what you need to do, but you still need to undo old habits and learn new ones. If you've been reading this book in sequence, by now you have anchored your motivation through a mindfulness topic, and learned and practised one or more mindfulness methods. This chapter will help you develop a sustainable mindfulness habit that you can solidly and meaningfully integrate into your life.

How Heroes Make It Happen

Remember the ordinary heroes you met in Chapter 2? I'd like to introduce you to six more. Each has been able to establish a mindfulness practice for at least three years. For some, this wasn't necessarily easy to achieve. These stories will illustrate how each person found his or her unique style, discovered ways to integrate practice into daily life and the supports needed to keep going.

SAM IS a skilled body worker who brings profound physical relief to his clients through the technique of Rolfing. He finds that his Native American heritage makes it natural for him to integrate mindfulness practice seamlessly into both his professional and personal life.

"At home I don't practise in a rigid way. That doesn't work for me. I have to stay aware of when Spirit calls me. Sometimes I'll be watching TV and a big emotion pops up, I don't know from where. I just mute the TV and go into that sacred space where I can experience the emotion in its totality. If it's grief, it's grief. If it's sadness, it's sadness. It could last five minutes or thirty minutes. When it's done, I just go back to watching my show.

"When I'm working on people, I'm focusing on flow. It's like mindfulness in action. I put my hand on their back, quietly sink in, then the tissue talks back to me with what it wants. I have to be very present in the moment. I often get deeper effects when I work with people this way, sometimes pretty amazing effects."

RICHARD IS a psychologist who became curious about mindfulness after seeing the changes in his sister, who took a Mindfulness-Based Stress Reduction course as part of her recovery from breast cancer.

"I was a dabbler for the first few years. I'm not very organized or disciplined. I'd go to a retreat, get a burst of enthusiasm, then fall off the wagon. This happened for a few years. What turned it around was finding a sitting group in my area. We met every week and meditated for around an hour. That put a solid foundation of practice in place. I added a goal of thirty minutes every day, which I would achieve about half the time.

"I'm pretty sceptical by nature, but I started to get evidence. How I was experiencing my life was changing, in a good way. I became a bit more present overall, more honest with myself about things I'd been avoiding. Now I practise about an hour a day, fitting it in when I can. It's harder when I'm travelling or on holidays. I was the wounded healer, with a tendency to get depressed. Now I'm helping people get better in my practice without getting burned out as much myself."

CAROL IS an academic researcher who rounds out her professional life with the martial arts of karate and aikido. She started mindfulness with breath practice but after a few months just stopped. Her second try was more successful.

"For my second try, I set myself a practice goal of twenty minutes a day early in the morning. I'd allow myself fifteen minutes of resistance to getting out of bed, then just did it. I also gave myself one day off a week, with my choice as to which day, so I didn't feel trapped in a routine.

"Now I've designed a one-hour routine that starts with yoga or physical work, then some intention setting or reading and then meditation. By the time I hit the cushion to meditate, my body feels better and I'm ready to go.

"I've noticed that my energy levels are way higher than they used to be. This surprised me, because it wasn't a motivating factor when I started. I'm more in tune with the choices I make during the day. When I go to aikido class, I'm able to be present for the full three hours. I can clearly see what the teacher is demonstrating, even if I can't yet do it. I'm bringing capacities that aren't typical at the beginner level or in a forty-six-year-old body."

LEAH IS an IT professional who brings a curious, geeky attitude to her mindfulness practice.

"I was first exposed to mindfulness during savasana at the end of my yoga class. Holy crap, I had no idea it was possible to feel so relaxed!"

Slowly, she became more interested in the psychological aspects of yoga, reading and taking several courses. At first, her practice was pretty sporadic, twenty to thirty minutes here and there. With time and the right supports, this solidified into a steady habit.

"What motivates me is charting and practising with my friends." Leah shows me her Excel spreadsheet tracking daily practice times. "It's like when I train for a run, or any other successful life habit. I'll set a goal, make a plan for how I'm going to reach that goal and then track my progress. I practise mindfulness thirty minutes daily, although last year when I had more time it was an hour each day. Life changes and you have to be flexible. I also started a weekly sitting group in my house. This was partly to introduce it to others, but mostly to help keep my own practice going.

"I used to think I was my thoughts; there was no separation. Now that's completely gone. I freak out way less about physical pain; now I just see it as transitory. But the biggest change is in how I come across to other people. I'm a type A, ambitious, hard-driving person. Now people tell me how calm and serene I am. That would not have happened ten years ago. And I'm more compassionate. Not that I was a witch, but I was more caught up in my own little world. People probably looked at me as a tough, walled-off chick. And now every week someone calls to share something with me. That is unrecognizable."

MINDFULNESS IS not a silver bullet; it may not be suitable for everyone at every time. Richard—the psychologist mentioned above—thinks that mindfulness may not be appropriate for people who are already psychologically vulnerable. Several of our heroes found that they needed to complement mindful awareness skills with other modalities, such as therapy or exercise.

Vera has been practising various forms of mindfulness for twenty years, as part of her personal-growth work and as an antidote to depression. She often felt that meditation wasn't helping that much.

"Last year when I was going through another bout of depression, a friend mentioned that for severe depression, meditation alone doesn't work. You need to add aerobics. I finally found a doctor who helped me get the right medication and now I exercise regularly. It's made all the difference. I couldn't access the teachings when I was depressed, but now I can.

"I'm a child of Holocaust survivors. I've had low self-esteem since childhood. I used to judge people a lot. Now I find that I'm not intimidated by anybody. My judgements of others just aren't there. I also had a real poverty mentality. If I went to a restaurant I would order the least expensive item. At some point that shifted. Now if I want something I get it, although I do look for value for the dollar. I just don't have that scarcity mentality anymore."

FIONA IS a medical scientist who grew up in the midst of violence during the time of the Troubles in Northern Ireland.

"As a teenager, I experienced the worst of the worst. Our family business was fire bombed. A gun was put to my aunt's head. I escaped through studying, so I didn't have to deal with the emotional stuff." She was initially introduced to the relaxation side of meditation through yoga classes. Years later, she went to a weekend mindfulness workshop and then took a six-week meditation course. Each was an amazing experience but somehow the practice never stuck. What turned it around were defined meditation techniques and the support of friends.

"I was sleeping poorly and would wake up in the middle of the night with my mind racing. Then it dawned on me I could use the Focus In method. As soon as I broke it into pieces—there's a body sensation, there's an image, there's internal talk—I realized I didn't have to get wrapped up in the story. It just totally disappeared."

Fiona found the combination of therapy and mindful awareness very powerful.

"Meditation opened me up to the emotional side of what happened during my youth. During one mindfulness class, I relived a horrible experience, recalling the second time our family business was bombed, after my brother had taken over from my parents. I had a complete meltdown, bawling my eyes out. But I knew I could talk about it later with my therapist. Without that support, I might have been too frightened to go through those kinds of experiences. I came to realize that I had been so walled off; I was living life without emotional connections."

Through a steady mindfulness practice, each of our ordinary heroes was able to realize extraordinary potentials in life. But what do you have to do to turn your good intentions into a steady habit?

Three Elements of a Sustainable Habit

As Charles Duhigg points out,[38] a habit is an ingrained pattern of behaviour that we rely on every day. It's a routine that, once learned, we do without thinking, like putting the left sock on before the right or our customary posture when we sit in a chair. Habits are stored as patterns wired into our brains. They allow our brains to be efficient and our minds to get on with other things, like thinking about an important meeting while driving to work. Changing habits, or inserting a new one, can be difficult. So it helps to understand what's involved.

There are three elements that create and reinforce a habit loop: a trigger, an automatic behaviour that results from the trigger and a reward that you experience from doing that behaviour. Consider my addiction to chocolate. Every evening shortly after I've finished supper (trigger), I get a craving for dark chocolate. I indulge in two squares of seventy percent chocolate, which I always have in the house (behaviour). Then I get the delicious zing of flavour (reward).

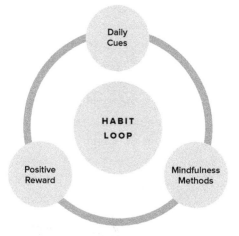

For mindfulness practice, there are three elements in the habit loop:

1   The daily cues for when and where you will practice (trigger)
2   One or more of the mindfulness methods that you practise (automatic behaviour)
3   The changes that happen over time (positive reward)

In Chapters 7 to 9 you learned various mindfulness methods. These are the behaviours you can practise. To establish a steady habit, you need to create daily cues that become triggers for "this is my time to meditate," when you implement the mindfulness method of your choice.

The Practice Map for Conscious Living in this chapter will help you set up these cues, so that you can select from a range of ways to integrate practice into your life. I'll illustrate how the map can be applied through several sample practice habits. Lastly, I'll guide you through designing your own Practice Map for Conscious Living. In Chapter 11, we'll review how to notice the positive rewards of mindfulness.

Practice Map for Conscious Living

Mindfulness is a skill for living, not a pill for instant relief. Like any skill, it takes repetition and practice. The challenge in mindful awareness is to build a skill deep enough to foster meaningful changes in your life and reliable enough to kick in when you need it. For most of us, the biggest problem is—no time. Acknowledging this, some teachers recommend a go-easy approach of ten minutes a day of practice. While this is a good place to start, I believe it carries risks. Ten minutes a day does not give you sufficient repetitions to rewire your brain, the opportunity to develop a new version of DAN or a habit deep enough to stick when the going gets tough.

The Practice Map for Conscious Living gives you a framework within which you can creatively design ways to get in enough practice repetitions to build a solid skill. By identifying different ways to organize your practice and by using a variety of mindfulness methods, you can address the risks of the go-easy approach while acknowledging the realities of your schedule. Should you wish, it is entirely realistic to be practising thirty minutes a day, thirty days from now. You can set your own goals and get creative in how you achieve them.

First, let's review the map itself. There are two scales that frame the map: how long you practise (the vertical axis) and how much of your attention goes to mindfulness practice during that time (the horizontal axis). This gives you two broad ways to organize your practice: formal practice and informal practice.

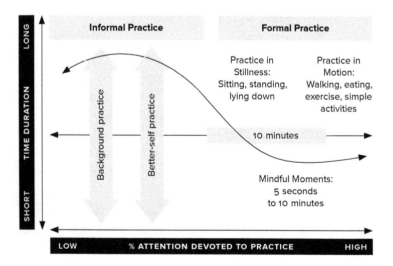

Formal Practice

When you imagine a meditator, you probably think of someone sitting quietly, possibly cross-legged with eyes closed. This is one way to do what I will call "formal practice." Formal practice has two criteria: Most of your attention is devoted to implementing a mindfulness technique and you practise for a minimum of ten minutes. But you don't need to be seated to do formal practice. You can practise:

1   In stillness, for example, sitting, standing, lying down
2   In motion, for example, while walking, eating, exercising or doing simple activities

Practise in Stillness is the anchor point of a mindfulness practice. Here you create a simplified environment so that you can focus all of your attention on learning a new mindfulness technique or going deep with one you already know. While seated may be the most comfortable posture, you can also practise standing or lying down.

If you are sitting, I recommend you start with a period of ten minutes. Then, as you get comfortable, increase this in small increments of up to twenty, thirty, forty minutes or more. If sitting still makes you too fidgety, you can alternate sitting with standing erect. If you want to prepare for a good night's rest, try meditating while lying down before bed, using a method such as Focus on Rest or breath practice.

Practise in Stillness has many advantages. The posture itself provides a feedback loop on how you are embodying the paradoxical qualities of being simultaneously focused yet relaxed. If you notice your back is slouched, you're probably too relaxed. If your back is arched or your chin jutting out, you're probably too tense. Any of the mindfulness techniques presented in this book can be applied while in stillness. Some techniques, such as Focus In, Focus on Rest or the Just Note Gone or Do Nothing techniques can most readily be practised in stillness.

However, practising *only* in stillness does have its limitations. It can be physically uncomfortable; your body may not be used to this posture or stillness may not appeal to you. (Remember Barbara's story from Chapter 2: With the busy mind of an attention deficit disorder personality, she initially found practising in stillness quite difficult.) If you only do Practise in Stillness, it may be more difficult to transfer mindfulness directly to your life challenges. The biggest challenge is that you can only find so many minutes a day to sit still. The solution? Ensure that you spend a minimum of ten minutes on Practise in Stillness and augment this with Practise in Motion and informal practice.

Practise in Motion is the second component of formal practice. Here you implement a mindfulness technique, again for a minimum of ten minutes, but now while you are moving around. This means finding situations that are so routine for you that you can devote most of your attention to your mindfulness method, not what you are doing. This gives you a lot of options! Walking, eating, brushing your teeth or washing your hands, during exercise or sport, playing a musical instrument, preparing a meal or doing simple chores are all opportunities for Practise in Motion. Many techniques work well with Practise in Motion: Feel-See-Hear, Focus Out and the body component of Focus on Rest or Focus on Flow.

Practise in Motion is an ideal way to get more practice repetitions in your day, allowing you to quickly build critical mass in your mindfulness skills. You could easily design a formal practice of thirty minutes using a combination of Practise in Stillness and Practise in Motion, for example, ten minutes in the morning sitting in stillness before going to work, ten minutes in motion while walking (to the bus, with the dog) or while doing a household chore or exercise (running, biking, workout, yoga) and a final ten minutes in stillness, lying down in bed before you go to sleep. The key is to pick simple activities that you do most days and devote most of your attention to your mindfulness technique during that time. Practise in Motion is both efficient and rewarding. It's a great way to turn dull parts of your day into something more lively and meaningful.

The risk of Practise in Motion is that it can quickly degenerate into "practice light." Since you are engaged in other activities, you have to contend with distractions. You can easily lose focus on your mindfulness technique. Let's say that while you are out walking you start off with eighty percent of your attention on See, of the Feel-See-Hear technique. Something distracts you—a sudden noise, thoughts about the meeting you had this morning, and poof—you are lost in automatic ruminations. The solution is to apply Practise in Motion to the same routine activities most days and to use labelling (spoken strongly internally or even voiced out loud).

Informal Practice

With "informal practice," you implement mindfulness techniques in small but meaningful ways throughout your day. If formal practice allows you to go deep in penetrating your consciousness, informal practice allows you to go broad, spreading mindfulness throughout your life. With informal practice, you relax one of the two criteria of formal practice. Either only *some* of your attention goes to the practice (the horizontal axis) *or* most of your attention goes to the practice but for short bursts of time, anything from a few moments up to ten minutes (the vertical axis). You can do informal practice in three ways:

1   Mindful Moments: using any mindfulness technique, for a few seconds up to ten minutes

2   Better-Self Practice: doing specific daily actions that activate your better self

3   Background Practice: applying any mindfulness technique in the background of your daily activities

Mindful Moments are those in which you apply micro-hits of a mindfulness technique during your day, a few seconds here, a few minutes there. The technique can be one you consistently apply at different times, or you can use different techniques for different situations. You can use one of the standard techniques given here or custom-design a sequence that works for you. Here are some examples:

- Using Feel or Feel Out to enjoy a meal or savour a particularly delicious piece of food (this is referred to as mindful eating)

- Using Feel In to consciously detect an emotion in your body, before it unconsciously hijacks you

- Using Focus on Rest during lulls in your day (waiting in line or for your computer to boot up) to help you de-stress and contact calm

- Using See Out and Hear Out to enjoy the buzz at the mall or the sights and sounds in a park or in nature

- Using Nurture Positive to prepare yourself for a difficult conversation, for example, visualizing a mutually favourable outcome or the positive qualities of the individuals involved

- Using Hear Out while enjoying music or using a combination of Hear Out and Feel In to attune to how your emotions respond to external stimuli

Mindful Moments can both enliven your day and bring heightened awareness to your daily challenges.

Better-Self Practice is intentionally implementing, in small ways, a value or positive behaviour you aspire to. This practice often appeals to action-oriented individuals and complements the Nurture Positive theme in Chapter 9. With Nurture Positive, you use mental intentions to shape consciousness from the inside out. With Better-Self Practice, you work from the outside in, deliberately acting out those higher intentions. Better-Self Practice is like the coaching exercises I give my clients; it involves ways to learn and apply new skills on the job.

These daily actions can help you practise whatever values or positive behaviours you aspire to: kindness, patience, generosity, good humour, forgiveness, love, compassion. The possibilities are endless. Smiling at someone, letting the other car pass you on the highway, offering hospitality, directing your gaze at the homeless woman on the street, making financial donations where you are able, attempting to see the point of view of someone you disagree with can all be part of Better-Self Practice.

Background Practice is an intermediate-level practice that you can do once you have some competence in the mindfulness skills of concentration, clarity and equanimity, and solid grounding in one or more of the mindfulness methods. With Background Practice, you spread some mindful awareness across your day; like butter on hot toast, you let it sink in. The key is to devote only some of your attention to a mindfulness method (horizontal axis) for several minutes or up to many hours a day.

For Background Practice, you consciously start a technique, and then let it run in the background of whatever you're doing. Some people like to do loving-kindness or a Nurture Positive practice as they walk through city streets or a country lane. I like to focus some of my attention on body sensations (Feel Out), keeping myself grounded throughout the day.

Informal practice can be easy to do, integrating mindfulness into your day in ways that are personally relevant. I wish I had discovered practising in this way much earlier in my own journey. It is easy to delude yourself into how mindful you are alone on the cushion; what is humbling is to realize how mindless you can be when you are upset with a child or frustrated by a customer.

On its own, informal practice can become "mindfulness light," with the quality of your attention slowly degrading. By combining the depth of formal practice with the breadth of informal practice, you have a sustainable habit that can transform your life.

Sample Practice Habits

To demonstrate how the Practice Map for Conscious Living can help you design your own mindfulness practice, here are several different examples. These are all based on real people, whether an ordinary hero like Rafael, my own experience or those of my clients. Treat these sample habits like a personal fitness routine, or a menu planner, giving you ideas you can customize for yourself.

Rafael: Breath and Body Movements

Rafael is a former teacher and basketball coach, now a writer. His introduction to meditation came more than twenty years ago, during his five-year stint as a competitive runner. He loved that expansive "runner's high" state that can occur in the middle of a good run. His practice reflects who he is: an active, creative, tell-it-like-it-is person.

Formal practice started with only five minutes, sitting on the edge of his bed. "It wasn't horrible," he says. Since then, he has gradually lengthened the amount of time and experimented with the best time of day to sit. A few years ago, it was before breakfast. Now it's after breakfast, first stretching to get physically comfortable, then sitting for thirty to forty-five minutes.

Much of his practice is informal, for example, mindful action while driving to and shopping in the supermarket. Through his Better-Self Practice, Rafael aims to cultivate gentleness as a counter to his naturally assertive, in-your-face personality. So he intentionally closes the clunky kitchen cabinet doors quietly, so as not to disturb the neighbours in the next apartment. Rafael used to long for a still mind. Now he has not only accepted his busy mind but has tapped into its creative potential. At one point, he designed an entire teaching workshop based on ideas that came to him while doing formal sitting practice. (Tip: Keep a notebook handy!) Rafael's primary methods are mindfulness of breath and body movements.

Office Professional: Meditation for Relaxation

Here is a sample practice for an office-based professional who has a busy but fairly consistent schedule and who started mindfulness practice as a way to de-stress and prepare for her day.

Her formal practice is sitting in stillness for ten minutes, six days a week. She sets her alarm to wake up early. She starts the coffee, splashes her face with water, then sits on a straight-backed chair. She does the Feel-See-Hear method, then ends with Nurture Positive. She adds another ten minutes just before she goes to sleep at the end of the day. Lying on her bed, she does Focus on Rest, which she finds helps her to get a good night's sleep. She adds another ten minutes three evenings a week when out for an evening run with friends, using Feel Out.

Informal practice is during the drive home. She turns the radio off and does See Out and Feel Out, *only* on those sensations relevant to driving (eyes on the road, hands on the wheel). She also does a few minutes of mindful breathing three to four times a day: while walking to the washroom at work or while the computer is slow to boot up. Her Better-Self Practice is also on the drive home as she consciously lets other cars cut in front of her if it appears they feel they need to.

Entrepreneur: Enhancing Equanimity

This sample practice helps a self-employed entrepreneur face the risks he is taking. It adapts well to his "no-two-days-are-the-same" schedule.

Formal practice in stillness is ten minutes, which he fits in most days, when he can, adding more time when possible. He starts with a few minutes of mindful breathing, then does Focus In, to befriend the emotional load he is carrying. He ends with Feel Rest, to build equanimity and to balance out his naturally vigilant mind. Practise in Motion is where his fun and reward is: Feel Out or Feel Flow, when that familiar "expansive or bubbly" sensation occurs during the daily run or workout.

Informal practice is an opportunity to get out of his head and into body sensations; he practises Mindful Moments of Feel Out during the morning shower and when washing his hands. But he mixes it up daily to keep it fresh. Better-Self Practice is making a point of looking someone directly in the eyes when talking, as a way to practise building empathy and better connections with people.

Stay-at-Home Parent: Caring for the Caregiver

Here is a sample practice for a stay-at-home parent with two young children. With slight modifications, it could be adapted for anyone with significant care-giving responsibilities, whether those are balancing work and family or caring for aging parents.

Formal practice is mostly done in motion, since toddlers don't sit still. Focus Out during the daily walk to the playground. Some moments of Practise in Stillness are snatched while the baby is sleeping, with the toddler on his lap; Feel Out on the delicious smoothness of the two-year-old's skin. When a ten-minute sit is possible, he settles in with breathing, then practises Do Nothing, as a counter to the hectic days.

Informal practice is done during the many routine household chores, such as See Out–Feel Out while cooking or Nurture Positive at random moments while looking at the kids playing. Better-Self Practice comes just before bed, when his doubts about his capabilities as a parent assail him. This sometimes takes the form of an inner affirmation, which he repeats internally to himself: "The kids will be okay."

Experienced Meditator: Refreshing Intent

Here is a sample practice for an experienced meditator whose routine has reached a plateau. He is wondering whether practice and his personal tendency to push through obstacles are distancing him from the uncomfortable parts of life—spiritual bypassing—rather than helping him be more present with all of life.

Formal practice while sitting is reduced from sixty minutes to forty-five minutes in the morning, with the same twenty minutes in the evening. He uses a variety of methods every few days, keeping a notebook handy to write down the differing effects after each sit. He keeps alert to the body, combatting a tendency to rigidity by regularly adjusting and softening body posture. His Practise in Motion is a combination of See Out and Nurture Positive as he's out walking every day. He incorporates Just Note Gone daily as a way to relax into natural endings.

His informal practice has several elements. TV or Netflix practice involves looking at shows, fully taking in all the emotions that are expressed and contacting the emotional sensations in the body through Feel In. Mindful Moments extends this with regular check-ins to areas in the body where he knows he carries emotions and tensions, again using Feel In. Better-Self Practice is putting himself in new situations outside of his comfort zone where he can be of service, for example, volunteering in a soup kitchen or homeless shelter. Background Practice is an inner mantra he uses while in the midst of crowds: "I see you: Be well."

Design Your Practice Map for Conscious Living

Congratulations! If you've made it this far you have all the tools you need to develop your own sustainable mindfulness practice. It's time to get creative and make it your own. But with so much to choose from—different mindfulness methods, different ways of organizing practice—how do you know what to choose? Here are some guidelines to help you develop a practice and personal supports so that you get through the inevitable ups and downs:

- Regarding which mindfulness method to choose, the most important guideline is that it doesn't matter. All the methods in this book develop the core skills of concentration, sensory clarity and equanimity. So pick whatever appeals to you. The more you enjoy, the more you will practise, the sooner you will develop mindfulness skills and taste the positive rewards.

- For formal Practise in Stillness, you can use one mindfulness method or several. You can use a standard sequence or mix it up daily. I like to ensure that I'm using methods from each of the three themes—Appreciate, Transcend and Nurture Positive—at least weekly.

- For Practise in Motion or informal practice, you can use one standard method that you like or different methods for different situations.

- Regarding ways to organize your practice, go for regularity and consistency of practice, using the same cues to develop a daily habit. Better a small amount regularly than occasional large bursts of practice.

- Once you've developed a small but stable base, extend it and mix it up. Practise a bit longer, using different methods, in different and more challenging situations. It's like adding weights in strength training; start off small, add challenge in increments, regularly push your edge. This way, mindfulness becomes a skill pervading your whole life.

- Learn to recognize rhythms in your practice: when to bear down and persist through obstacles, when to ease up and let experience come to you.

- Put in place positive supports. With our ordinary heroes, you've seen that different supports worked for different people. These supports can include: books that inspire or teach, guided meditations, apps, notebooks for journaling, support from your friends, a buddy you check in with, taking a class, joining a sitting group, setting up a place at home to sit that includes helpful gear, such as a straight-backed chair or meditation cushion and a timer.

- Do periodic intensive practice. Going on a meditation retreat—from a few hours to a week or more—is an experience like no other. The guidance of the teacher and the energy from practising with a group will support you, while the duration of practice will challenge you. The right combination of support plus challenge creates an optimal growth environment.

- Do periodic check-ins with a qualified coach or teacher. Meditation can be a lonely business, in which it can be hard to register progress. Find someone with appropriate credentials that you can relate to and who can teach you methods, guide you in applications to your life and challenge you in your blind spots.

WITH THESE guidelines in mind, it's time to develop your own Practice Map for Conscious Living.

First, recall your motivation for why you are interested in practising mindfulness. This may be the same topic statement you developed in Chapter 5, or you may have revised it since then.

Your Mindfulness Topic Statement

[Future Vision] I am interested in practising mindfulness because I would like to be more able to

_____

_____

_____

_____

[Present Discomfort] This is important to me now because

_____

_____

_____

_____

Now develop what you think would be a reasonable practice goal. Remember that with the range of mindfulness techniques and all the options of the Practice Map for Conscious Living, thirty minutes a day is entirely doable.

My Practice Goal

Now write down how you can reach your mindfulness goals. (For the sake of simplicity, I have not included Background Practice.) For each item, note cues and tips such as where, when or how long.

My Practice Map for Conscious Living

	Where, When, How Long
FORMAL PRACTICE	
Practise in Stillness	
Practise in Motion	
INFORMAL PRACTICE	
Mindful Moments	
Better-Self Practice	
Helpful Supports	

You now have a customized design to launch, guide and support you on a mindfulness journey. But how do you know if it's working? It may take some time to notice positive rewards. They may be easy to see—or not. These are the questions we will turn to in our final chapter.

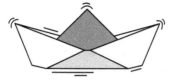

[11]

Resilience and Flourishing

Y OU'VE NOW understood the basic skills of mindfulness,
learned one or two methods that cultivate these skills and
developed a practice approach that works for you. How do
you know if it's working? This is the third element of the habit
loop, one essential for maintaining your motivation. If you diet,
you're supposed to lose weight. If you exercise, you're supposed
to get strong or flexible. What is supposed to happen with mindfulness practice?

Being in a state of mindful awareness while you're practising can be enjoyable and rewarding in itself. You can learn to
detect and enjoy the distinct flavours: a sensation of calm and
strength that comes from concentration, a vividness that comes
from clarity and an acceptance that comes from equanimity. But
the proof of "is it working?" should be found in your life, not in
your experiences while meditating.

For many successful habits, the reinforcement comes from
the presence of a positive, like the flavourful burst of tasty food,

the tautness of flattened abs, the connection with others in healthy, if sometimes difficult, conversations. Reinforcement of the meditation habit is different. Progress in mindfulness comes not so much from the presence of a positive as the absence of a negative. It is a counterintuitive approach. But once you know that you are supposed to evaluate it by looking in the rear-view mirror, not at the road ahead, it becomes much easier to track changes and progress.

So you need to be asking yourself, "What has changed? Is there something that used to bother me that now bothers me less? Am I getting new kinds of comments or feedback from others?" At first, the changes may be small and sporadic; with time they become larger and consistent. You have developed a new normal.

You anticipated some of these potential changes when you developed your Mindfulness Topic Statement. They could include specific muscles of resilience, such as persistence, staying focused under pressure, handling unpleasant feelings, more connection with people or a greater sense of self-control. They could include broad outcomes, such as better functioning in life, a relief of suffering or increase of fulfillment, greater awareness of yourself or broader compassion for others. These are very helpful in setting your direction and anchoring your motivation, but they don't necessarily predict where you will end up. Your mind is not a simple linear tool, so be prepared to be surprised!

Here are more of our ordinary heroes, who tell of the surprising effects of mindfulness in their lives.

CHRISTINA RECENTLY retired as a C-suite executive in the financial services sector. She started mindfulness ten years ago, as a preventive measure prior to taking on a big job she knew would be stressful.

"What surprised me was that the first changes were physical. That first class, when we did body scans and a whole body relaxation, I found the pain in my ankle was reduced. My physiotherapist told me the muscles in my leg were more relaxed. My dentist said the muscles in my face were more relaxed. I used to be a master fidgeter; now my body is relaxed most of the time. It certainly helped me be a better leader than ever before. I had to lead us through a difficult period of layoffs; I found I was listening to others differently, with less of my own agenda in the conversation.

"I also discovered early on that I was carrying a lot of emotional baggage. In the financial industry it can be okay to stab your colleagues in the back. I used to joke that I'll just take the knives out of there, to make room for more. When that first bit of baggage left, I knew what it was. Later on, you don't always know the content of what's leaving. I used to carry ugly old emotions half the size of a soccer ball in my gut. Now that's just gone. Mindfulness has led to a physical feeling of lightness. Unfortunately, that doesn't show up on the scales!

"It's also made a big difference in my relationships. People do the same stupid stuff they always did, but I respond differently. My family said I had to come back to classes!"

SABRA IS a freelance journalist who started practising mindfulness four years ago, when friends invited her to a local class. She was intrigued by the mind-altering potential of meditation.

"I saw the effects on the cushion quite quickly. The inner narrator would quiet down. I realized that this was actually possible, not necessarily a default of existence that I was stuck with. If I meditated long enough, the words would break up into shards of sentences. What has changed is my tendency to go unconscious and daydream. My mind has been in that groove for thirty years, tugged in the direction of images, memory or fantasy. Now I catch myself in the act of daydreaming and bring myself back. I've been told I do it less; I do know I'm more present with people.

"What is surprising is that I'm more in touch with emotions. Now I can feel everything more: love, anxiety. Before I would have said, 'Open my heart to what? I haven't killed anyone, so what's the problem?' But I couldn't commit fully to anything; pursuing a direction, being in a relationship. I didn't know what I was feeling. Mindfulness has broken me open in an unexpected way."

What does it mean to have an absence of a negative? What happens when physical tensions, emotional baggage or disconnects with others are dialled down? It means there is a direct impact on your personal resilience. Remember the definition of resilience? "Resilience is the ability to recover, adapt and grow in response to threat or challenge." If there are fewer negatives in your life, you have fewer challenges to overcome and therefore you have more energy to creatively adapt and grow. Less demands on your finite capacities of resilience means greater opportunity for natural flourishing to occur, for innate talents to blossom.

Reducing the negatives is like scrubbing away blockages in your inner circulation. In your body, arteries that are free of plaque permit the circulation of oxygen-rich blood from your brain to the tips of your toes. You are healthy. But when plaque accumulates, your arteries harden, blood flow is restricted and your health is impaired. You are at greater risk for heart attacks or stroke. You can prevent hardening of the arteries through lifestyle changes, such as healthy eating, exercise and stopping smoking.

Mindfulness does for your subjective life what healthy habits do for your body. It cleans away the debris in your psyche. With greater mindfulness skills—MoMo enhanced—you can observe and appreciate *all* of your experience. You know how to have a complete experience: an awareness that can digest anything that occurs, leaving behind no residue (like in Linda's story below). Or you have tools to clean out long-standing emotional baggage (as is seen in Chantal's story below). Less internal debris means you have a broader bandwidth available for how you live your life. You don't become a different person; you become more of who you deeply are.

BROUGHT UP in a traditional Catholic environment, Chantal is now a senior manager in government. She started meditation thirteen years ago, when travelling in Nepal after her divorce.

"I told myself not to make meditation complicated. I just pay attention to the breath and the body. This journey was about developing a relationship with myself. At first, we try to get away from the unhappiness in our lives; for me it was a failed marriage and a difficult childhood. I wanted peace and acceptance, but I was looking for it in other people. I found it in myself. Did you know that your feelings start in your body, then you label them in your mind? Mindfulness is like sitting quietly with your body, finding out what it's saying to you. I want to tell people, 'Shake hands and say hi! [You and your body] are made for each other.'

"I was seeing a therapist who knew the vulnerability and shame work of Brené Brown.[39] I told her, 'In my body, there is a filing cabinet and in one of the drawers is a Shame Box. I want to take it out and examine each file, each piece of shame.' Mindfulness is courage. In order to look at the files of shame, you have to stop to be mindful of it, to stay present with it. It's not saying, 'This is how I am and I cannot change.' That is being attached to your past. Letting go of the past is one of the hardest things to do. Meditation helped me do it."

A GENTLE, small-boned woman, Linda started mindfulness twenty years ago, to cope with neck pain she acquired during the time she was program director at a cancer recovery centre. It helped her with everyday stress reduction.

"Meditation has helped me be more at peace, more patient. I absolutely know I can be with unpleasant sensations and not get freaked out. It's a tool for keeping me sane and honest. But I may be less charming! In my family, we valued the quick wit and sharp comeback. I've lost that capacity for mindless banter."

It's for the big threats and big questions that Linda has found she relies on mindfulness.

"A few years ago, I was in bed at home alone when I was robbed. I was able to have a complete experience of it, with no resistance. I saw two figures outside my door, marching toward my study. There was no way for me to escape. I sat up straight and out of my belly a deep, fierce voice boomed 'What the fuck are you doing?' Then I got up and walked into the living room; they were running away into their car. They'd taken my computer, wallet and keys. My identity. And that night, I slept like a lamb. I never got scared. I was just okay.

"I'm beginning to realize I'm going to die. It's more than an intellectual idea. I'd be lying to say that I'll be able to be present with whatever comes up. But I can't think of anything other than meditation that would help. Where else do you get to do this kind of inner work? Where else do you learn to sit with discomfort? People say 'gardening is my meditation.' That's just words. Where else do you truly stare at this moment in life?"

SOME PEOPLE have come to mindfulness when facing the ultimate threat: their own mortality. Kate had a big career in marketing, steadily climbing the ladder, putting in sixty to seventy hour weeks over an eighteen-year career. It was stressful, but she loved it and was good at it. When the first two wake-up calls occurred, she altered professional course—a bit. The third wake-up call was a rare, aggressive and advanced breast cancer. Four years later, after four surgeries, chemo and radiation, Kate is well. During that time she discovered mindfulness, the relationship between stress and disease and the impact of mindfulness on stress. She took a Mindfulness-Based Stress Reduction course and hasn't looked back. Kate now leads "Wake Up Kate" as a corporate mindfulness coach.

"I realized that stress didn't cause my cancer but did inflame it and make it worse. I cannot describe the life-changing impact of that realization. It was like I woke up. I realized I had been living on autopilot, a classic, ladder-climbing, want-it-all working mom. But I wasn't prepared to give up what I had tasted through mindfulness. I realized that if you want to make changes in the world you have to start with changes in yourself. It was counterintuitive because before I always put career and kids before myself.

"At first my motivation for practice was cancer, but with every clean bill of health that motivation decreases. Now I've added accountability structures such as classes, groups and friends. Really, all excuses not to practise are just a way of saying it's not important enough to you. Now it's routine for me. Intention setting in the morning, formal practice at lunch and Mindful Moments during the day. I use mindfulness with my kids all the time. My son has learned, rather than to punch someone, to say, 'I'm feeling very angry.' I felt like jumping up to the sky when I heard that."

An absence of negatives is like an absence of walls—within yourself and between you and others. By being aware of more of yourself, you befriend all of who you are, including the bits you'd rather not be reminded of. Your different selves can talk to and get to know one another, become integrated. You are more comfortable in your own skin. From the outside, it may not look like much. But you and I know it's huge.

MEDITATION TECHNIQUES used to be for the privileged few. East and West, monks and nuns practised contemplation in a religious context to transform themselves and their relationship to God. Like treasures, the methods were safeguarded and passed on through the generations. These methods worked, but they relied on rigid structures, specific belief systems and the support of many lay people to sustain a secluded life for a select few.

This privileged focus has changed. Mindfulness is now accessible for anyone who wants it. Not just religious people, not just the privileged few at the top of the social ladder, not just for those who choose to step off the ladder entirely. It requires no specific belief system or cultural background. Mindfulness is being practised by adults and children, by working people and students, by the sick and the healthy. This broadening of access is a significant advance. But every forward wave of advance has the potential for an undertow.

By broadening access, we risk watering down the heft and rigour of the original methods. How do we recreate the conditions that originally made transformation possible without going back to the old days? Modular, scalable approaches like Unified Mindfulness can do this. You can practise fifteen to twenty minutes a day and through Mindful Moments gradually expand this so that you become more mindful throughout your day. A comprehensive approach respects the inherent complexity of your mind, and makes it more accessible.

Says Andrew, a forty-year meditator who has practised in Christian, Buddhist and secular settings, "I understand far more of what happens in meditation and I attribute that almost entirely to Unified Mindfulness. It helps to know what you're experiencing and how to get back there. Before, inner silence would emerge at random. I would have to go on retreat for two to three days before the mind would quiet down. Now I find that noting and labelling is a quick fix. If I sit down and label 'Hear In' once or twice, I'm off to the races."

Any significant technical or social change can lead to unexpected impact. When residential air conditioning was introduced to Florida in the 1920s, it promoted a population explosion, the climate now rendered more livable. When new outdoor technical gear was developed in the 1970s, it fuelled a boom in adventure camping and travel, now made affordable and comfortable. Mindfulness is at the cusp of creating a similarly significant change. I am deeply grateful for what this change has meant to me. I am awestruck by the stories of our ordinary heroes. I wonder, if my brother John had known about this, might he have found his way?

What might mindfulness change for you? It could be as simple as one more act of persistence along your chosen road. One deadline during which you stay focused and calm. One less stressful event; not because your life is stress free but because you know how to metabolize stress so it doesn't become distress. One difficult emotion you can handle, not because you are unfeeling but because you know how to feel. One simple insight or creative new idea, not because you think better or faster but because you don't over-think. One instance of shared laughter with someone you hadn't suspected you could connect with.

These small instances add up. You recover better from challenges; your life naturally flourishes. You find yourself, incrementally, living with greater freedom, generosity, courage and kindness. You mind your life—and life minds you back.

Recommended Reading

Begley, Sharon. *Train Your Mind, Change Your Brain.* New York: Ballantine, 2007.

Bourgeault, Cynthia. *The Heart of Centering Prayer: Nondual Christianity in Theory and Practice.* Boulder, CO: Shambhala Publications, 2016.

Epstein, Mark. *The Trauma of Everyday Life.* New York: Penguin Books, 2013.

Goleman, Daniel. *Emotional Intelligence: Why It Can Matter More Than IQ.* New York: Bantam, 2005.

—————. *Focus: The Hidden Driver of Excellence.* New York: Harper, 2013.

Harris, Dan. *10% Happier: How I Tamed the Voice in My Head, Reduced Stress Without Losing My Edge and Found Self-Help That Actually Works—A True Story.* Toronto: HarperCollins Canada, 2014.

Joiner, Bill and Stephen Josephs. *Leadership Agility: Five Levels of Mastery for Anticipating and Initiating Change.* Toronto: Jossey-Bass, 2007.

Kofman, Fred. *Conscious Business: How to Build Value Through Values.* Boulder, CO: Sounds True, 2006.

Livingston, Gordon. *Too Soon Old, Too Late Smart: Thirty True Things You Need to Know Now.* Boston, MA: Da Capo Press, 2008.

Scharmer, C. Otto. *Theory U: Leading from the Future as It Emerges.* Oakland, CA: Berrett-Koehler Publishers, 2009.

Tolle, Eckhart. A *New Earth: Awakening to Your Life's Purpose.* New York: Penguin Books, 2008.

Wilber, Ken. A *Theory of Everything.* Boulder, CO: Shambhala Publications, 2000.

Young, Shinzen. *The Science of Enlightenment: How Meditation Works.* Boulder, CO: Sounds True, 2016.

Appendix

PRACTICE SUPPORTS

Summary of Practices

Noting

1 Noting consists of a rhythmic pulsing of deep acts of attention, paced in a way that works for you (for example, every three to five seconds). Each pulse has two parts:
- An initial noticing or acknowledging of a particular sensory event
- A short period of intently focusing on that experience

Note Everything in Feel-See-Hear

1 Let your attention go to whatever sensory experience arises or calls to you. This could be any aspect of somatic, visual or auditory space.

2 Begin the rhythmic sequence of noting. If you wish to use labels, they are "Feel," "See" or "Hear."

3   If all or part of a sensory experience suddenly drops or disappears, and you happen to notice it, you can choose to use the label "Gone."

Focus Out

1   Let your attention float between physical body sensations, sights and sounds. Work with whatever is available. If more than one is available at any one time, just choose one to note.

2   Note according to what you are paying attention to, "Feel Out," "See Out" or "Hear Out."

3   If something that you are focusing on suddenly drops away, and you happen to notice it, note "Gone."

Focus In

1   Let your attention float between emotional-body sensations, mental images and mental talk. Work with whatever is available. If more than one is available at any one time, just choose one to note.

2   Note according to what you are paying attention to, "Feel In," "See In" or "Hear In."

3   If something that you are focusing on suddenly drops away, and you happen to notice it, note "Gone."

Focus on Rest

1   Let your attention float between restful physical- or emotional-body sensations, the defocused gaze of grey-scale blank of visual rest and the exterior silence or inner quiet of auditory rest.

2   Note, accordingly, "Feel Rest," "See Rest" or "Hear Rest." If restful states are available in all three spaces, use the label "All Rest."

3   If a rest you are noting drops away, and you happen to notice it, note "Gone."

Focus on Flow

1   Let your attention float between fluctuating, changing or flowing experiences in somatic, visual or auditory spaces.

2   Note, accordingly, "Feel Flow," "See Flow" or "Hear Flow."

3   If all or part of any flow experience drops away, and you happen to notice it, note "Gone."

Just Note Gone

1   Let your attention freely float among any or all body, visual or auditory experiences.

2   Whenever all or part of something drops away or drops off, and you happen to notice it, note "Gone."

Do Nothing

1   Let whatever happens, happen.

2   Whenever you are aware of an intention to control your attention, drop that intention.

Nurture Positive

1   Decide on which of Feel Good, See Good or Hear Good you'd like to work with.

2   Anchor yourself by tuning in to any pleasant emotional-body sensation, creating an appropriate mental image or repeating internally a short phrase.

3   Direct this sensation, image or phrase in ways relevant to you, such as positive behaviour change, fulfilling relationships, healthy thinking patterns or emotional states you'd like to encourage.

Practice Journal

Your Mindfulness Topic Statement

[Future Vision] I am interested in practising mindfulness because I would like to be more able to

_____

_____

_____

_____

_____

[Present Discomfort] This is important to me now because

_____

_____

_____

_____

_____

Practice Log

Date	How Long	Method (formal, informal, technique...)

End of Practice Notes

- Log what you practised, for how long.
- What supports are helping you?
- How do you feel at the end of practice?
- Any insights you want to capture?

End of Week/Month Reflection Questions

- Any physical changes?
- Any negatives in your life that are no longer as present?
- Any new capabilities more available?
- Any feedback from others?
- How might you want to fine-tune your practice for next week/ month?

Notes

1   See Shinzen Young, *The Science of Enlightenment: How Meditation Works* (Boulder, CO: Sounds True, 2016).

2   "Mindful Nation UK: Report by the Mindfulness All-Party Parliamentary Group," The Mindfulness Initiative, http://www.themindfulnessinitiative. org.uk/images/reports/Mindfulness-APPG-Report_Mindful-Nation-UK_ Oct2015.pdf (accessed February 3, 2017).

3   Ibid.

4   Bondolfi et al., "Unpublished Report, 2014" (lecture by Dr. Zindel Segal, A Mindful Society's 2015 conference *Integrating Mindfulness in Society: Health, Education, Work and Life*, Toronto, Canada, March 28–29, 2015).

5   See Edmund Metatawabin with Alexandra Shimo, *Up Ghost River: A Chief's Journey Through the Turbulent Waters of Native History* (Toronto: Alfred A. Knopf Canada, 2014). See also Alexandra Shimo, *Invisible North: The Search for Answers on a Troubled Reserve* (Toronto: Dundurn, 2016).

6   See James Maskalyk, *Six Months in Sudan: A Young Doctor in a War-Torn Village* (Toronto: Anchor Canada, 2010) and *Life on the Ground Floor: Letters from the Edge of Emergency Medicine* (Toronto: Doubleday Canada, 2017).

7   "American Mindfulness Research Association," www.goamra.org.

8   See Jon Kabat-Zinn, *Full Catastrophe Living: Using the Wisdom of Your Body and Mind to Face Stress, Pain and Illness* (New York: Bantam Dell, 1991).

9   "Mindful Nation UK."

10   Judson A. Brewer et al., "Meditation Experience Is Associated with Differences in Default Mode Network Activity and Connectivity," *PNAS* 108, no. 50 (November 23, 2011): 20254–59, doi: 10.1073/pnas.1112029108.

11   Britta K. Hötzel et al., "Mindfulness Practice Leads to Increases in Regional Brain Gray Matter Density," *Psychiatry Research* 191, no. 1 (January 2011): 36–43, doi: 0.1016/j.pscychresns.2010.08.006.

12   Michael D. Mrazak et al., "Mindfulness Training Improves Working Memory Capacity and GRE Performance While Reducing Mind Wandering," *Psychological Science* 24 no. 5 (March 2013).

13   Eileen Luders, Nicolas Cherbuin and Florian Kurth, "Forever Young(er): Potential Age-defying Effects of Long Term Meditation on Gray Matter Atrophy," *Frontiers in Psychology* 21 (January 2015), doi: http://dx.doi.org/10.3389/fpsyg.2014.01551.

14   "Unpublished research by Dr. Richard Davidson" (presented at Mind and Life Summer Research Institute, Garrison Institute, Garrison, NY) reported in Garrison Institute blog, July 23, 2015, https://www.garrisoninstitute.org/?s=rapid+recovery+resilience+and+the+braiN&Post_type=post.

15   J.D. Creswell et al., "Alterations in Resting-State Functional Connectivity Link Mindfulness Meditation with Reduced Interleukin-6: A Randomized Controlled Trial," *Biological Psychiatry* 80, no. 1 (July 1, 2016): 53–61.

16   Madhav Goyal et al., "Meditation Programs for Psychological Stress and Well-Being: A Systematic Review and Meta-analysis," *JAMA Internal Medicine* 174, no. 3 (March 2014): 357–68, doi: 10.1001/jamainternmed.2013.13018.

17   Stephan G. Hofmann et al., "The Effect of Mindfulness-Based Therapy on Anxiety and Depression: A Meta-Analytic Review," *Journal of Consulting and Clinical Psychology* 78, no. 2 (April 2010): 169–83, doi: http://doi.org/10.1037/a0018555.

18   Goyal et al., "Meditation Programs for Psychological Stress and Well-Being."

19   "Mindful Nation UK."

20   P. La Cour and M. Petersen, "Effect of Mindfulness Meditation on Chronic Pain: A Randomized Controlled Trial," *Pain Medicine* 14, no. 4 (April 2015): 642–51, doi: 10.1111/pme.12605.

21   Yi-Yuang Tang et al., "Short-Term Meditation Training Improves Attention and Self-Regulation," *PNAS* 104, no. 43 (October 23, 2007): 17152–56.

22 Antoine Lutz et al., "Regulation of the Neural Circuitry of Emotion by Compassion Meditation: Effects of Meditative Expertise," *PLOS One* 3, no. 3 (March 26, 2008): 1–10.

23 See Paul Condon et al., "Meditation Increases Compassionate Responses to Suffering," *Psychological Science* (August 2013). See also www.headspace.com.

24 Mathias Dekeyser et al., "Mindfulness Skills and Interpersonal Behaviour," *Personality and Individual Differences* 44, no. 5 (April 2008): 1235–45.

25 See Bruce W. Smith et al., "The Brief Resilience Scale: Assessing the Ability to Bounce Back," *International Journal of Behavioral Medicine* 15, no. 3 (February 2008): 194–200. See also, "The Connor-Davidson Resilience Scale Revised," CD-RISC, http://www.cd-risc.com/index.php.

26 Daniel Goleman, "Resilience for the Rest of Us," *Harvard Business Review*, April 25, 2011.

27 Maria Konnikova, "How People Learn to Become Resilient," *The New Yorker*, February 11, 2016.

28 See Daniel J. Siegel, *Mindsight: The New Science of Personal Transformation* (New York: Bantam Books, 2011).

29 See Mark Epstein, *The Trauma of Everyday Life* (New York: Penguin Books, 2014).

30 Joanne Hunt, "Transcending and Including our Current Way of Being," *Journal of Integral Theory and Practice* 4, no. (2009): 1–21.

31 Robert Kegan, *In Over Our Heads* (Cambridge, MA: Harvard University Press, 1994).

32 See C. Otto Scharmer, *Theory U: Leading from the Future as It Emerges* (Oakland, CA: Berrett-Koehler Publishers, 2009).

33 Norman A. Farb, Zindel V. Segal and A.K. Anderson, "Mindfulness Meditation Alters Cortical Representations of Interoceptive Attention," *Social Cognitive and Affective Neuroscience* 8, no. 1 (January 2013): 15–26, doi: 10.1093/scan/nss066.

34 See Daniel Kahneman, *Thinking, Fast and Slow* (Toronto: Anchor Canada, 2011).

35 See Ken McLeod, *Wake Up to Your Life: The Buddhist Path of Attention* (New York: HarperCollins, 2001).

36 Trafton Drew, Mellisa L.-H. Võ and Jeremy M. Wolfe, "The Invisible Gorilla Strikes Again: Sustained Inattentional Blindness in Expert Observers," *Psychological Science* 24, no. 9 (September 2013): 1848–53. See http://search. bwh.harvard.edu/new/pubs/DrewVoWolfe13.pdf.

37 Amy Cuddy, *Presence: Bringing Your Boldest Self to Your Biggest Challenges*, (London: Orion Publishing, 2015).

38 Charles Duhigg, *The Power of Habit: Why We Do What We Do and How to Change* (London: William Heinemann, 2012).

39 See Brené Brown, *The Gifts of Imperfection: Let Go of Who You Think You're Supposed to Be and Embrace Who You Are* (Center City, MN: Hazelden Publishing, 2010).

Index

M EG SALTER offers mindfulness coaching and executive coaching to those who want to create positive change in their world. Based in Toronto, Canada, she provides distance coaching globally to individuals or groups.

All coaching is founded on a customized, integral approach that helps clients develop sustainable skills, allowing them to decrease frustrations, boost resilience and turn aspirations into reality. A professionally certified coach, Meg also has an extensive business background and deep experience in meditation.

Meg has been meditating since 1995, gaining profound experience while pursuing a career and raising children. Teaching since 2002, she has witnessed the enhanced resilience and personal flourishing in those who develop mindfulness skills, with beneficial effects on their colleagues, friends and families.

Meg holds an MBA from Boston University Brussels, and is accredited as an Integral Master Coach™, a Professional Certified Coach with the International Coach Federation, and a Certified Senior Organization Development Professional. She has a thirty-year professional background, working as a senior business manager and, through MegaSpace Consulting, providing change management consulting and executive coaching. She has lived in the UK and Belgium, consulted to multinational corporations, and distance-coached individuals across North America, and from Europe to Dubai. A committed volunteer, Meg's board and pro-bono work focus on newcomer integration, community building and individual empowerment.

Learn More

Meg Salter offers both in-person and distance coaching. No matter where you are in the world, if you have a phone or the internet and want to pursue what you have learned in this book, mindfulness coaching is available for you. For additional resources, or information on individual coaching, group coaching or training, visit:

www.megsalter.com

CPSIA information can be obtained
at www.ICGtesting.com
Printed in the USA
LVHW030917171218
600727LV00001B/4/P

9 780995 936805